CREATIVE COPING
A Guide to Positive Living

CREATIVE COPING

A Guide to Positive Living

by Julius Fast

with the assistance of Barbara Fast

William Morrow and Company, Inc.
New York 1976

Printed in the United States of America.

1 2 3 4 5 80 79 78 77 76

Library of Congress Cataloging in Publication Data

Fast, Julius (date)
Creative coping.

Bibliography: p.
1. Mental hygiene. 2. Stress (Psychology)
I. Title.
RA790.F314 613 75-28231
ISBN 0-688-02993-0

DESIGN: H. ROBERTS

For my brother Jerry

Contents

Introduction

How many times have you thought, I just can't cope with things? How many times have you heard your friends say, "I can't handle the kids . . . My job's too much . . . that wife of mine . . . that husband!"

There is a way of managing life, a better way to deal with the everyday crises of living, and this book is designed to explain that way, to describe the basic structure of the new, growing science of *coping*.

Today's world is an overwhelming one. Many of us find it difficult and often impossible to cope with the new life-styles, the new values, the economy with its rising inflation and shrinking job market, the political upheavals, and our troubled cities.

All of these side effects of our civilization build up anxieties, often too much for us to handle. While a little anxiety can be a good thing, acting as an impetus to make us cope better, too much can stop us from coping at all. The thinner our coping ability is stretched, the greater the buildup of anxiety until eventually it turns in on us and destroys us.

Physicians try to solve the problem by using tranquilizers to reduce our anxieties. Psychiatrists try various therapies to help us cope effectively. But both often ignore the fact that the very act of coping can reduce the anxieties and allow us to deal with life realistically.

For many years now, the National Institutes of Mental Health has concentrated on the problem of coping in the face of stress. Groups of scientists at the Institutes, at Stanford University in California, and at Tufts Mental Health Clinic in Boston have built up a tremendous bibliography on the subject. Some years ago, a conference on coping and adaptation was held in Palo Alto, California, to pool the nation's knowledge of the new science and set guidelines and objectives for therapy.

This book has drawn from these sources, as well as many others to present a coping model of behavior, a technique for reducing anxiety so we can be free to deal with the everyday occurrences of life as well as the greater, more dramatic ones; the Life Stress Crises.

These crises are stress situations that overwhelm all of us at different times, in childhood and adolescence, during adulthood in the thirties and forties, and in later years, in the menopause and the climacteric.

To survive these Life Stress Crises, a person must cope with life while learning to adapt, but still keeping a high level of self-esteem. Coping is a means of adapting to any difficult situation. It may not always solve our problems for us, but if we cope we are never completely overwhelmed by the problem. The usual result is a compromise, but one we can live with comfortably.

Everyone copes every day of his life. The baby copes from the moment he's born. He discovers that crying brings attention, food, comfort—so he copes by crying. How he'll cope as he grows up depends on how his early coping efforts are received. If no one picks him up when he cries, he becomes withdrawn and apathetic like institutional babies. If he's picked up and fussed over, then he'll be encouraged enough to keep relating to other people, first by crying and then by being a lively, interested baby.

How well we cope is often a combination of what we learn plus what we're born with. The baby with strong lungs cries harder and louder than another, and he's a bit ahead of the game.

But through all our coping efforts, we have to think well of ourselves. You can't cope to your best ability unless you have a good, healthy respect for yourself, according to Professor Robert W. White, social psychologist at Harvard University.

Our self-esteem is developed early in life, and in the beginning it's just a reflection of how our parents and friends see us. As we grow more independent, we begin to evaluate ourselves regardless of what others think.

A study in the magazine *Scientific American* showed that children who were good students and popular with their friends thought a lot of themselves. They were also darned good copers. On the other hand, the children who didn't think much of themselves were poor students and poor copers.

Other studies have picked up on this and found that the primary responsibility for being a good or bad coper lies with our parents. Parents who set limits, but were democratic about enforcing them, who listened to their children and were genuinely interested in them, produced kids who thought a great deal of themselves. They had a healthy dose of self-esteem.

These children are autonomous. They do things on their own and they're independent. They set their own limits and cope with life of their own accord. When they grow up they remain good copers.

Each of us is different and each has a different method of dealing with life, but all of us use certain basic coping elements such as aggression, flexibility, empathy, reason, masking, and control. But we all must have a high level of self-esteem if we intend to cope creatively. The methods and examples in this book are a healthy beginning.

[CHAPTER ONE]

Coping Strength: Life on Elm Street, USA

Elm Street is an ordinary street in an ordinary American town. The people who live there have the same problems we all have, and while most can handle them, a great many can't.

Amanda Robbins, for instance, couldn't handle hers. Young and attractive, Amanda always seemed to be full of life, but for the past two months she's been in and out of the hospital. When she's at home she's under a doctor's care and pumped full of tranquilizers. She tried to kill herself when her husband died of a sudden heart attack.

"I can't face it!" she kept screaming after the suicide attempt. "I don't want to go on!" It's sad, because Amanda has two young children and a whole life ahead of her.

Down the street there's Joe Freeman. A good family man, Joe. Easygoing and everyone's friend, only now he's up to his neck in legal trouble. Last spring, after leaving church, he got into an argument over a parking spot and he flipped out. He was hauled into court for assault and battery.

Then there's Emmet Murphy who lives with his family, watches a lot of TV, and does odd jobs around the neighborhood. Emmet was a Big Man On Campus in High School, on the football team, in the honor society—

head of his class. When he was accepted into a highly competitive college, everyone was sure he was headed for the top. Instead, he dropped out after the first semester. That was two years ago, and he hasn't been able to take hold of anything since.

But the real tragedy on the street happened one quiet autumn evening when Jim Gonzales shot his two sons and his wife and tried to blow out his own brains. The town isn't sure which is the greater tragedy, what he did or the fact that he survived. The policeman who got to the house first found Jim dazed, wandering around with blood streaming from his head, repeating, "I couldn't take it, I couldn't take it!" over and over. He was still repeating it when they took him to the hospital. Jim had lost his job with the automotive parts plant eight months before, and he hadn't been able to find another job since.

Elm Street covers a lot of territory, and there are many other people on it. They aren't all losers. For every Amanda and Emmet there are a dozen others who can cope with life. They have no trouble with the day-to-day frustrations, and they even handle the bigger problems and tragedies.

There's the principal of the high school who claims the problems of integration have turned his corridors into literal battlefields. He fights the school board, the town board, the parents and the students, and he grins and says, "I'll fight even my wife!" The funny thing is, he thrives on the battle.

Sol Fine in the big house on the corner lost his wife and son in the same car accident, and a week later his married daughter died of cancer. He manages. He still runs his hardware store and he does volunteer work as a scout leader for the boys in his neighborhood.

And then there's Mary Anne Kowalski. She's divorced and the sole support of her four kids. She's been out of work for three months, but she and her family are managing. They have unemployment, and her oldest boy hustles some work after school. As a family, they're coping.

A REACTION TO STRESS

Back when World War II ended, only psychologists and schoolteachers talked about coping. Now the word is part of everyone's vocabulary. Has the world changed so, or have we suddenly become aware of our own deficiencies? It's probably a little of both. People have always had a tough time dealing with their lives, but as the world becomes more and more complex, we find there are more Amandas and Emmets and Joes and Jims, and fewer Sols and Mary Annes.

As "Future Shock" takes hold, we find that life begins to fragment and fall away. What we could handle five years ago is now too much for us. Even the definition of coping has changed. It used to be a synonym for managing, but psychiatric usage has broadened it to include *the way we relate to our environment and to the people we live with.* It includes all the strategies and tricks we pull out of our mental hats to master situations and adapt to stress in a stressful world.

Fifty years ago Walter Cannon, a Harvard physiologist, described our physical response to stress as "Flight or Fight." The heart beats faster, the blood pressure rises, body metabolism increases, and blood flows to our muscles.

Flight or fight was nature's way of helping animals cope with threatening situations. Now, in our complex civilization, stress causes the same physical symptoms. If we can cope, they subside. If we can't they take their toll by permanently raising our blood pressure.

In spite of this, stress is an integral part of coping. It's the stimulus that arouses the coping ability, and conversely, coping is one of the ways we react to stress. It's a good way and a positive way.

Most of us are able to deal with mild stress, with the everyday frustrations of life. A shopper misses a bus, a wife upsets her husband, a parent scolds a child, a traffic jam delays a commuter—these are all minor annoyances and simple to handle.

But the more difficult the stress, the harder it is to cope. Overwork at the job, constant bickering in a marriage, an overdrawn bank account, a girl ignored in a singles bar—the stress mounts. Coping is not so easy.

And then there are the severe stresses, the things that drove Amanda and Jim to desperation. Someone we love dies. We lose our job. Our marriage turns bitter and hateful—the stress mounts to a point where it takes a great deal of strength to manage.

But what one man manages another can't, no matter what the degree of stress. Emmet couldn't deal with the moderate stress of college. Joe couldn't deal with the very minor stress of being cheated out of a parking place. He saw it as a threat to his manhood and reacted in a primitive way with his fists. His tolerance to stress at that moment was incredibly low. Mary Anne Kowalski's tolerance to stress, in any situation, was enormous.

This relationship between stress and coping—coping as a way to manage stress, and stress as a trigger to the coping ability—is a relatively new idea.

MANIPULATING LIFE

Psychiatrists used to believe that we reacted to stress by avoiding, repressing, or denying it. This was the Freudian viewpoint. In a number of articles and lectures during the past fifteen years, Dr. Robert W. White has stressed the fact that everyone is born with the potential to manage stress, to cope, but not everyone makes the most of that potential.

The ability to cope can be knocked out of us at an early age by overprotective parents, critical friends, inadequate schools, and poverty—or any of the other forces that mold us as we grow.

However, when these forces are good they can strengthen our coping ability. We can learn to be a success instead of a failure in dealing with life. Our coping can be positive instead of negative, competent and creative instead of destructive.

We can separate the wrong coping methods from the right ones only when we understand the conscious and unconscious forces that move us. We must not let life push us around. We have to take hold of it and manipulate it. That's creative coping.

If there is one rule above all others in learning to cope, it's to put a proper value on yourself. The man who knows his own worth is most likely to decide things for himself, to be a free agent instead of a tool, to be autonomous.

He makes up his own mind and he's responsible for himself. He's also able to choose the right coping techniques.

To change our coping patterns, we have to learn how and when they start. Most are tangled up with our childhood, and in an attempt to unravel that tangle, the Menninger Foundation and the United States Public Health Service set up a study of coping some twenty years ago.

It was intended to be a longitudinal study, a cross section in time, and it was labeled the *Coping Project.* Psychologist Dr. Lois Barclay Murphy headed it, and announced that its goal was to find out how children learned to cope.

Dr. Murphy and her associates studied thirty-two

children between the ages of two and a half and five and a half. They followed them into their homes, became friends with their parents, and watched them at school and play, trying all the time to learn how they handled situations that were different, strange, frightening, agreeable, usual or unusual.

"Why," the Menninger researchers asked, "are some children able to face new situations calmly and competently while other children are completely overwhelmed by the same incidents? In short, why can some children cope better than others?"

SAM'S FINGER

One child in Dr. Murphy's study who was able to cope with disaster was Sam. He was only three years old, bright and full of life and mischief. At a birthday party a friend slammed a door on Sam's finger and the tip was cut off.

Sam stared in terror at the welling blood, and then started to scream. After one look, his mother whipped a napkin around the finger and rushed Sam to the hospital, holding him in her arms while a neighbor drove. As the pain of the severed finger replaced the shock, Sam's screams changed to a childish whimper, and he clung to his mother desperately, begging for his blanket.

While the doctor cleaned the finger and stitched it together, Sam kept acting more and more babylike and helpless. "He's not much of a big boy," the doctor ventured, trying to shame Sam into bravery.

His mother shook her head firmly. "He doesn't have to be now. I'm here." She held him close, comforting him, and let him cry and fuss as much as he wanted. "It's just too much for a child his age to handle," she told the doctor. "He can cry all he wants."

Sam made the most of it, but only for a while. As the pain diminished, he straightened up and became the "big boy" the doctor wanted. His mother offered to hold him on the ride back, but Sam shook his head. "I'm all right now."

During the next few weeks, when he visited the doctor, Sam's mother went into the examining room with him. But after a while, she decided that it was time he went in alone. Still, she didn't want to appear the one rejecting him. "You tell him I'm not allowed in with him anymore. The doctor wants to see him alone," she told the nurse.

The nurse agreed, and at first Sam resisted this forced independence, but strengthened by the fact that his mother had let him rely on her all along, he gave in. The real turning point in his recovery came when he began to play carelessly with his old friends. The accident hadn't made him overcautious or fearful.

What helped Sam cope with his accident? Where did he get the strength to be a "big boy" so soon and go back to his regular, carefree life?

Dr. Murphy believes Sam's strength came from his mother and the way she handled the incident right from the start. She hid her own panic and acted calm and unworried. She let Sam depend on her when he needed her, and she let him do it without shaming him.

When he was ready to move away and stand on his own feet, she let him do it without holding on. She let him go at his own pace.

Because of this, Sam learned a good method of coping with all problems that are overwhelming. Stand back from a difficult situation until you have the inner strength to manage it.

Many children do this instinctively. They will watch a new set of friends, or a new playground, clinging to their parents, until they are sure of themselves and the situation. Then they'll move in to play. The parent who tries to force them before they are ready deprives them of some of their coping ability.

NATURE OR NURTURE?

Sam's story shows us that our ability to cope is influenced by our parents' actions, by how they handle us when things get tough. We learn tricks of coping in childhood and use them all our lives.

But are we forever locked into these tricks? Can they be changed? Can our coping strength be increased? Can we learn new coping techniques?

The answer is yes in three cases. To be human is to be able to change your habits and your patterns of behavior. Anyone who has lived through the last ten years is aware of that.

We're all born different, but from the day of our birth, and even before that in our mother's womb, environment works to change us even more. Intelligence flowers with education—withers with ignorance. Poor nutrition stunts a healthy body. Disease, pollution, and bad habits cut our lives short.

We don't know which is more important, nature or nurture, but a current view offered by Marston Bates in the journal *Anthropology Today* suggests that environment guides us one way or another while our genetic background sets the limits on how far we can go. Some poverty-stricken people turn into criminals; others, just as poor, become good citizens. One man's meat, in a sociological sense, is another man's poison.

Every baby is born with a given amount of coping strength that grows stronger or weaker depending on what happens along the road to adulthood.

Some babies are friendly and full of laughs. Others

are apprehensive and cry when they see a stranger. They are born with these differences, but they can change. The outgoing child can become apprehensive if someone hurts her, while the apprehensive baby can be reassured with gentleness.

How a baby copes with a stranger depends on how that stranger copes with the baby, and the same law holds true as the baby grows up.

Some children respond quickly, others slowly. Let's take a look at Sara and Philip. Both babies were breast-fed by their mothers, and both mothers always drew the curtains before feeding time. Sara very soon learned that a darkened room meant that her hunger soon would be satisfied. She stopped crying the moment the curtains were drawn.

Philip, however, never seemed to learn this. He'd scream up to the moment his mother's nipple entered his mouth.

Perhaps Sara learned more quickly, or perhaps Philip felt hunger more keenly, or it may be that Philip's way of coping, from the very beginning, was to yell bloody murder when he didn't get what he wanted.

As Sara grew older, she remained tractable and easy to manage. If her mother promised her a treat tomorrow, she would wait in patient anticipation. Not Philip. He'd tear the room apart until he got what he wanted.

Here we have two different coping styles, and each worked. Philip's mother gave in easily, and this strengthened his behavior. Sara's mother always kept her promise, and this strengthened Sara's behavior.

It's an intriguing fact that Sara and Philip did their own thing, from the first day of their lives. Not every part of personality is inborn. Philip might have changed the way he acted if his mother had held out against his tantrums. He would have had to find other ways of coping. Sara might have given up on patience if her mother had broken her promises, or if the first time Sara tried a tantrum it worked. It didn't. Her mother walked away and Sara never tried it again.

THE COPING SEESAW

What it all boils down to is that each child copes with the world around him in his own way at his own pace, but—*in turn, that world also copes with the child and changes the child's ability to further cope with the world.* A coping seesaw is set up.

When things are quiet and under control, when the seesaw is at rest, the child will often start it rocking again. He will deliberately look for trouble in order to create new situations he can cope with. This isn't getting into mischief for mischief's sake. It's setting up a problem that he can try to manage. For most children, coping is an enjoyable play-learn process. They find the challenge of a new situation fun and games, and they set about dealing with it eagerly. They enter school with anticipation. They just can't wait to get involved.

This is the way it should be, but not all children are like this. Many need long periods of adjustment before they can handle new situations. To them, school is a threatening experience. There are too many new children and unfamiliar tasks. They need to pull back like Sam. He had to retreat and gather his strength before he could manage the problem of his damaged finger.

In order to cope with life, a child must handle two situations. He must handle the situation *within* himself—hunger, fear, curiosity, excitement, or anything else that affects him. And he must also handle the situation *outside* himself—school, his parents, his friends, his neighborhood—in short, the world around him.

What a child can cope with also depends on what he can get, on what he understands of his world, and on how his body can manage that world. One little girl may want some delicious cookies in the cookie jar up on the kitchen shelf, but for all her wanting she may not be physically able to push a chair over to the counter, climb up and unfasten the lid of the jar. All this must be possible before she can cope with the problem.

A normal, healthy physical development helps a child develop coping techniques. A bad digestion, poor eyesight, hearing troubles, all can hinder coping. Indeed, most children have some physical problem, big or small, that prevents them from becoming perfect copers.

Dr. Murphy, in her coping study, notes that the "fully and serenely developed child, able to use all his functions optimally, able to handle all the demands put on someone his age and able to respond to all the opportunities offered is an abstract ideal."

He just doesn't exist, and if he did he would be an insufferable little robot!

[CHAPTER TWO]

Aggression: A Coping Tool or a Danger Sign?

THE IMPORTANCE OF AGGRESSION

How important is aggression in coping with life? We can't answer this question properly unless we know what part aggression plays in everything we do. But while we can't tell *exactly* how important it is, we do know that it's one of the most important parts of the human condition. Aggression is involved in every task or job we undertake. It's behind every artistic or scientific creation. It's the force that moves us forward in life.

Unfortunately, aggression has been given a bad press. When we hear the word, all the ugly aspects of it come to mind—war, hostility, robbery, and murder. Sure, these are all examples of aggression gone wild, but aggression under control is one of the strongest coping tools we can use.

Judith is a wife and mother and a very aggressive young woman, but Judith's aggressiveness has always been a help to her family. When her husband's job took the family to a new town and they relocated in a house in the suburbs, the family could have easily faced a lonely period of readjustment. But instead, the first day that she settled in, Judith visited her neighbors on each side, introduced herself, and without being too pushy managed to make friends.

Within a month Judith was active in a local political organization to fight pollution of the nearby river, and she had volunteered to be a den mother for the cub scouts. The family was integrated into the community in no time flat.

"My wife is a real go-getter!" her husband said proudly, but Judith shook her head. "The alternative was to sit home and wait for the world to come to me, which it just wouldn't do."

Judith's aggressive drive is well-controlled. It gives her just enough push to make life comfortable for her family. "She's busy enough with all these projects so that she doesn't bother me," her husband says. "She doesn't try to run me like other wives do."

We all should have, like Judith, a healthy amount of aggression to fuel us along life's track. Some wives have this normal amount, but unlike Judith, they can't use it in productive ways, getting to know the neighbors, being active politically or socially, or in part-time or full-time work. They must keep their aggressive outlets within the family and become dominating wives or mothers—or they bottle up their aggression until it spills over.

Bottling up aggression, of course, isn't restricted to wives. Men do the same thing. In a newspaper recently there was a story of a young husband who had to be cut out of a wrecked car with an acetylene torch. He had crashed into a concrete abutment.

"I don't know why I was speeding," he told the police on his hospital bed. "I had an argument with my wife and I was angry with her."

"Did you hurt her?"

"Hurt her! God, no. I love her. I didn't even yell at her. When I yell she bursts into tears and I can't stand it. No, I slammed out of the house and got into my car and burned rubber. I was boiling over and I had to get out on the road and drive—to get it out of my system.

I don't know where I was going or even how fast. I was just so furious . . ."

"It's a common story," the police investigator said. "A guy can't get rid of his anger, so he drives it out in his car and gets reckless and stupid."

This husband could have worked out some way of showing his anger instead of bottling it up. He could have redirected it to his work or life away from home instead of letting it spill over into a dangerous night ride.

His wife, had she been able to cope with his aggression either by fighting back or turning it aside, might have helped. By resorting to tears she forced him to bottle it all up. But is there any good way to cope with someone else's anger?

TURNING ASIDE WRATH

Animals have instinctive devices to disarm an aggressor. A young puppy will roll over, exposing its naked belly and letting a drop of urine appear. The odor of the urine turns off an older dog's aggression. Baby chicks use a continual cheeping noise to turn off their mother hen's natural aggression to anything small. Deaf hens who cannot hear the cheeping will peck their own chicks to death.

Are there similar devices for turning off aggression in humans? Has nature built inhibitors into us, and if so, are they still in operation in spite of our civilization?

Well, some inhibitors are present. It's hard to stay angry with someone who apologizes profusely. It's hard to be aggressive to someone who's amiable. Both amiability and apology are "turn off" devices.

Some people believe nonviolence is an effective device for turning off violence or aggression. They reason that if you don't fight back, it becomes harder for someone to fight you. Identification is still another "turn off." If the aggressor identifies with the victim, he finds it hard to be hostile.

A friend of mine stepped into an elevator in a large office building and found, once the door had closed, that he was alone with a heavyset, menacing young man. "The way he looked at me," my friend said, "I knew I was in for trouble, and he was between me and the emergency bell. He started toward me and I thought, this is it!"

"What did you do?"

"I moved in before he could say a word. I came on strong and friendly. Maybe I even babbled. I said, 'Hey, what do you think of the Jets? That Namath is great, isn't he? Hey, do you play football? You know, you've got a fullback's build?' I just kept on like that till we reached my floor, and he didn't know what to say. I gave him a wave and got off. I don't know if he was a mugger or not, but I didn't give him a chance to be anything."

My friend used identification to turn off aggression. Instead of an anonymous target, he became a sympathetic human being. He could still have been mugged, but the other man was thrown off balance by his friendliness. He hesitated, and his chance was lost. It's much harder to be aggressive toward someone you can identify with.

A perfect example of this happened recently in Sweden. An escaped convict held three women and a man hostage in a Stockholm bank for almost a week. The hostages were finally rescued unharmed. The curious thing about the incident was the unusual identification that grew between the hostages and the convict. In prison, after the incident, the convict was asked by a reporter, "Did you actually have it in mind to kill the hostages?"

"In the beginning, I could have easily," the convict

answered thoughtfully. "After I gave up, there were police who told me that if I had killed just one of the hostages, I could have gotten a plane out of Sweden. But I didn't need the police to tell me that. I knew it myself."

When pressed, he continued angrily, "It was the hostages' fault. They did everything I told them to do. Why didn't any of them attack me? They made it hard to kill. There was nothing to do but get to know each other, and then who could I kill? Elizabeth, helpless and crying? Kristin, full of spirit? Sven, a decent, brave man? Birgitta, who couldn't get those kids of hers off her mind?"

Identification had done its job.

There are other ways of coping with someone else's aggression, psychological ways such as withdrawing completely, turning inward, refusing to listen. Children often use these devices against aggressive parents when they have no other weapons of defense; husbands and wives use them against each other, but for the most part these are negative coping devices. If they do work, they leave you less of a person.

When we consider aggression in terms of coping, there is not only the problem of coping with other people's aggressions, but also of coping with our own inner aggressions. As children, we may be taught that it's wrong to be angry, and we may grow up believing that and bottling up our aggressions.

Gina was a classic example of dammed-up aggression. Gina considered her marriage to Mario a happy one. She did everything he wanted without complaining. She cooked, kept house, and built her life around Mario's whims. She never seemed to mind changing her plans to suit him, calling off dates when he was tired, going where he wanted to go and doing what he wanted to do.

Periodically, however, she'd get into a fit of temper. She'd walk around the house sullen and muttering, slamming doors and dropping dishes, and finally exploding in a fit of screaming, yelling, and tears.

When the outburst was over, she'd calm down and be the old Gina again. "I don't know why I do it," she'd apologize, "but afterwards I always have this beautiful, peaceful, serene feeling."

She'd become more yielding than ever to Mario and settle down for another long stretch of self-sacrifice. Gina coped by holding back her aggressions until they exploded. She got by with it, but each blow up hurt her marriage a little more.

THE MODEL SON

Tony was someone else who held things in—obedient, polite, and always ready to put his parents' wishes first. Even when he was a child, his mother used to say, "Tony's such a good boy, so even-tempered."

But in adolescence Tony's even temper turned to moodiness and long bouts of depression. In college Tony had trouble during his first year because of a gastric ulcer. He suffered from continual colds and tension headaches, and at the end of the year shocked the college with an attempted suicide.

There was a terrible fuss, his parents confused about why such a "good boy" would do something like that, and finally the college agreed to keep him on if he'd see the school psychiatrist.

"Tony was a very angry young man," the psychiatrist said in his report. "He was forced into the role of a 'good boy,' never allowed to show his hostility or anger. As a result, he turned his anger inward, becoming depressed and ill, and finally tried to destroy himself.

"Actually, Tony's suicide was a call for help. His big fear was that he'd hurt someone else first. Fortunately we got to Tony in time!"

The Tonys of this world—the "good boys," the obedient children who never argue back—are the ones most likely to flare up once, and only once, in some devastating release of aggression.

Then we read about the young sniper who kills a dozen neighbors, the son who takes a rifle and murders his entire family, the daughter who hacks her parents to death with an ax.

At one stage in Tony's cure, he asked the psychiatrist, "How can I go around yelling at someone every time I'm annoyed? I can't be aggressive all the time. Hell, what kind of a world would it be if everyone did that?"

"No, we can't blow off at every annoyance," the psychiatrist explained, "but we don't have to. Most small aggressions can be controlled—but never forget that too much control can be dangerous."

HANDLING OUR INNER AGGRESSIONS

How can we strike a balance with our aggressions? People who lose their temper at every petty annoyance are impossible to live with, and yet people who keep every anger and aggression under wraps can be just as wrong.

Ideally, we should release our aggressions without feeling guilty ourselves or arousing too great a reaction in someone else. And we must know at what point discharged aggression becomes necessary for our own well-being.

What are the therapeutic techniques offered for discharging bottled-up aggression? One is primal scream therapy, yelling it all out and reliving the time when it was suppressed. Basically, this is playacting. You set up an internal stage set, recalling the original situations that made you hold back, and you yell it all out to an audience of fellow sufferers who will understand your problem.

For some people, primal scream therapy works; for some, it doesn't. It seems to work best when the aggression has been dammed up for too long and needs some outlet.

Another positive device for coping with internal aggression is talking it out, not necessarily with the person you're mad at, but with anyone who is understanding and sympathetic.

Still another device is rechanneling your aggression. Some men and women turn to sports to help discharge aggression. They can also turn to those areas of politics or business where a more-than-average supply of aggression is needed to succeed.

THE INTERNAL AGGRESSION QUOTIENT

It might be a good thing if all young people were measured for their internal aggression quotient (IAQ) and then directed toward those careers that require high or low IAQs. It may be a dangerous idea because it smacks of the controlled state of fascism, but at least it would help everyone to have some idea about his own IAQ.

A simple test of ten questions will give you some idea of where you rate aggressively on a scale of 1 to 10. It's far from an exact test, but answering the questions with complete honesty will at least give you some insight into your own aggressive drives.

If you score 9 or 10 on the test, you should look for some positive means of discharging your excess aggression. If you score less than 5, you should be aware of your need for more aggression in coping with life. Here are ten situations. Each has an A or B answer. See which you would honestly follow, and score by adding up the As and Bs you have checked. Ten As mean you're too aggressive to tangle with; ten Bs means you aren't aggressive enough to go out of doors alone. Most sensible and sensitive people will score about 5 and 5.

INTERNAL AGGRESSION QUOTIENT (IAQ) TEST

1. You are standing in line at the movies waiting to buy your ticket. It's a cold night, but there are enough seats. Someone pushes in ahead of you.

   A. You tap them on the shoulder and remind them that there's a line, that you were here first and would they please either go to the end of the line or, if there's some reason they must buck it, at least to get behind you.

   B. What the hell. It's a cold night and it won't kill you to be one back in line. After all, there are plenty of seats, so you say nothing.

2. You get on a city bus and all the seats are taken and the front half of the bus is crowded with people standing. The back, however, seems almost empty.

   A. You grit your teeth and push through the crowded front of the bus, ignoring the hostile looks and remarks, or perhaps answering, "Why not be sensible and step to the rear?" At the back you relax and enjoy the elbow room you've won.

   B. You realize that pushing to the back is going to be just as uncomfortable as standing in front. So, rather than upset everyone and yourself, too, you hang on with the crowd in front. You haven't all that far to ride, and with so many people pressing against you, at least you can't fall over.

3. You're driving along on the new superhighway when

some clown in a new Corvette Stingray whips past and cuts right in front of you, forcing you to jam on your brakes and be thankful you're wearing your seat belt.

A. Five minutes later, when you have a clear lane available, you step on the gas and rechallenge him, slip past and cut back in front of him.

B. You curse him out roundly, but let up on the accelerator and let him get far ahead, not wanting to have anything to do with a driver like that.

4. You come home from shopping to find that you've been overcharged by a small amount.

A. You go back to the store and raise hell about it.

B. You figure the amount of money isn't worth raising a fuss over. You should have counted your change more carefully, and you will in the future.

5. It's been a hard week at the office, with an enormous amount of work to be accomplished. While going through the accounts you see that a fellow worker has made a stupid mistake.

A. You show him the mistake and ask him how the hell anyone could do something that foolish when you're all so pressured to finish the job.

B. You correct the mistake yourself and forget about it. Everyone's under pressure, and why shake up a fellow worker?

6. You're married and you've just come back from an evening at a friend's where your husband/wife made an absolute fool of him/herself in an argument about something completely unfamiliar to him/her.

A. You read him/her the riot act, explaining just what a fool such wild generalizations make him/her out to be.

B. You figure it's really not worth going into, because sure as God made little green apples he/she will do the same thing again.

7. After dinner and over coffee you have a discussion

with your parents about today's youth, and your father makes some sweeping generalizations you can't agree with.

A. You catch him up on them and point out that his generation is into the same mess with alcohol instead of grass.

B. You know that whatever you say won't change his mind, so why antagonize him. You change the subject tactfully.

8. At a party you see the kind of a guy/gal that really turns you on. Unfortunately, he/she's with someone else. Still, there are signals.

A. You move in gently with charm and somehow let him/her know where you can be reached, and that you're interested.

B. You figure that there's not much chance of making time when he/she's with someone else, so you shrug and look around for second best.

9. That empty house next door is finally sold and the family has moved in and looks fairly settled. They also seem to be your own age.

A. Once the van has gone and the curtains are up, you stroll over and introduce yourself and welcome them to the neighborhood.

B. You wait for some natural situation to occur, a situation that will allow you to meet them casually.

10. You're at a pleasant cocktail party and a friend points out Mr. Big, a well-known figure who's extremely important in your own field. It would mean a lot to you to meet him.

A. You walk over and introduce yourself and attempt to impress him with your good qualities, enough so he'll remember you when you meet in a business situation.

B. You realize it would be in rather poor taste to strike up an acquaintanceship for business reasons, so you wait patiently for the host or hostess to bring the two of you together.

THE AGGRESSIVE SEX

When we consider the IAQs of both men and women, we generally find that men are more aggressive. Of course, there are many women with IAQs higher than most men, and many men whose IAQs are lower than most women. But in general, men are the more aggressive sex. Volumes have been written from either the *male chauvinist* or the *feminist* viewpoint proving or disproving this.

Animal behavior offers only flawed clues. In some species the male is the aggressor, in others, the female. The only thing proved is that the potential for aggression is present in both sexes. Among humans, almost all societies favor male aggression, and men and women grow up expecting men to be the more aggressive. However, in those few cultures where women had the upper hand, they developed as much aggression as men develop in our society. No clear-cut answer to the question—how much aggression is inborn and how much developed—has ever been given, and it's quite possible that none ever will.

What is important is that we understand that no matter how either sex acquires it, aggression is a necessary element in coping with the world around us, and women as well as men can and must develop it and use it. Take Sandra as a case in point.

Quiet, unassuming, and unattractive, Sandra worked as an editor in a large publishing house. She was good at her job, probably better than most of the men on the floor, but she wasn't pushy. She had grown up in a very normal, midwestern family, and she had always realized that her father and brothers were the real decision makers, the wage earners, and the outspoken ones. She and her mother, from the superior position of womanhood, pampered them by deferring to them. "Men," her mother often told her, "need to feel that they're leading us. The wise woman controls her man by letting him take the lead."

Even after she left home and went to work in Chicago, Sandra followed her mother's advice. But somehow she never felt that she did any controlling. At work she held herself back and saw one male editor after another move up past her. Yet she knew, deep down, that she was as talented as most, and more talented than many. It was only aggressive push that she lacked.

Sandra might have gone on for the rest of her working life turning her aggression inward, feeling bitter and depressed about her lack of advancement, if her publishing firm hadn't bought an ordinary little vegetarian cookbook at Sandra's urging. At best they thought they might break even on it, and low-girl-on-the-totem-pole Sandra was selected as the book's editor.

The book, thanks to Sandra's editing skill and a lot of breaks, took off and hit the best-seller lists, and Sandra was towed along with it, the "smart little editor who had seen its potential." In a few short months, she found herself sought out, courted, and constantly pulled into conferences. Other publishers tried to steal her away, and she became a person instead of a quiet little mouse.

Spurred on by her success, she took chances on some long shots, and one or two worked. Nothing succeeds like success, and as Sandra hit each success she became a bit stronger, a little more aggressive and a little surer of her own worth. An aggressive feedback took over. Confidence primed Sandra's IAQ, and as her aggression grew, her ability developed.

As Dr. Lois Murphy pointed out in her coping

study, environment develops the aggressive drive. Given one success, a woman can go on to push for another. She can feel secure enough to keep trying, to compete with men and win or lose on her own merit, not on the society's judgment of men and women.

Sandra was able to do this because of a lucky break. Very few women, talented as they may be, get the break. Most have to force the issue. I have two friends, a husband and wife who are both doctors, but Bob is known as Dr. Altchek and Ruth as the doctor's wife, Mrs. Altchek.

"I'm caught in a bind," Ruth told me, half joking and half serious. "If I insist on being called Doctor, I'm a bitch and splitting hairs. If I ignore it, I feel resentful, not only of the people who don't dignify me with my title, but of Bob, too. Just because he's a man he gets the respect he deserves. I'm every bit as good an M.D., but I'm a woman. Even our doorman calls him Dr. Altchek and me Mrs. Altchek!"

Ruth solves the problem by pointing out, usually with humor, that she, too, is a doctor. "I joke about it with friends and the family, but I get angry and annoyed with my colleagues. That title means a lot to me. I worked hard to get it."

Justifiably, Ruth resents the fact that she has to use more aggression than Bob to get what she deserves. "Why should I have to? Just because I'm a woman? I know I should say to hell with them all. I know my own worth. I suppose I should choose my battlegrounds, not waste my time fighting for respect where it doesn't matter, and to an extent I do. I usually give up with friends, but I keep fighting at medical meetings. That's where it really matters."

To cope with the situation, Ruth must raise her IAQ above the level with which she's comfortable. In the same way, once Sandra became sure of her own ability, she was able to force herself to act aggressively. But both women were using aggression artificially to cope with the world. They weren't comfortable with the amount of aggression they used, but they knew they needed it to get what they wanted: respect, acclaim, a decent salary, and advancement.

Men find it much easier to keep a high IAQ once they achieve it, but this is because society accepts aggression in men and frowns on it in women. Ruth and Sandra are successful, but they pay the price of defying society. Inevitably, someone jealous of their accomplishments will label them emasculators for no other reason than that they have successfully challenged men at their own game.

RAISING YOUR IAQ

Accepting the fact that to both Ruth and Sandra the important thing is success—much more important than what the male-oriented society thinks of them—the question arises, must they always use an artificial aggression to succeed? Must they always operate above their comfortable IAQ levels, or, to turn it around, what must they do to raise their IAQ so that they can cope without pretending?

What they can do is what Sandra, to some extent, has already done. They can strengthen their inner selves and allow their natural aggression to surface. A healthy aggression comes from a real knowledge of one's own worth.

It's also true that in some cases an excess of aggression is due to the very opposite, to a sense of insecurity about one's self. This is the sort of inferiority complex that makes a man act superior. But this is the exception.

The first question to consider in attempting to raise your IAQ is *what is blocking my natural aggression?* Most people have an adequate amount of aggression, but for one reason or another it may be blocked off. In most cases the block is fear. Those of us with low IAQs are afraid of disapproval or afraid we might lose the love and affection of our friends and family if we show our true feelings. The child begins to hold back aggression for fear of punishment, of parental anger or disapproval. Once the pattern is set, the adolescent and adult continues in the same routine.

My husband doesn't like pushy women. I'm afraid the other guys in the office will think I'm out to shaft them. My girl will think I'm just after her body. In each case there's a fear that too much aggressive behavior will turn other people against us. It's a valid fear, but the problem is, how much aggressive behavior is too much? Well-adjusted people automatically know how much to use. People with no confidence in their own worth are always uncertain, afraid they're using too much, or too little. They aren't aggressive enough, or they're overaggressive, overpowering.

The fear of one's own destructiveness can also cripple us in our coping patterns. The fears run: *If I am too aggressive I may hurt someone. If I lose my temper I'll explode altogether. Too much aggression will blow out whatever restraints I have. I'd be overwhelmed if I let myself go.*

And along with this there is a third fear. *I might enjoy it. I might get a kick out of aggression, out of overwhelming someone, out of imposing my will on another person. If I really enjoyed it, where would I stop? How would I know what limits to set?*

But these are fears the comfortably aggressive person doesn't have. His aggressiveness is so much a part of himself that he uses it without being aware of it. His IAQ is high enough so that he doesn't have to question his actions. Using the right amount of aggression is his normal behavior.

Once we become aware of the blocks to natural aggression, and once we understand them, then we are on the road to removing them. We can examine our own actions in the light of the realization that aggression is a healthy force. We must question our motives and expose them to the light of rational thinking. If we haven't handled a situation with enough aggression, then we must dig out the reasons.

What were we afraid of?

Did we think we would lose someone's love? Respect? Approval?

If we did lose it, how much does it matter? Which is more important to us, the love of those around us or the goals we are trying to reach? Is it worth taking a chance with love and approval to reach those goals?

And, most important, why are we prone to think someone will stop loving us or will withhold their approval if we show aggression to get what we want?

USING AGGRESSION CREATIVELY

Aggression is one of man's best coping tools, if he can learn to separate it from hostility—if, in fact, he can learn to tame it and use it. The error many people make is in bottling up aggression to the point where it becomes explosive. Then one chance remark or incident can set off an unfortunate reaction.

In the world we live in, it often becomes necessary to cope with other people's excess aggression. We cope by learning the ways of turning off others' aggression and then we concentrate on how to handle excess aggression in ourselves.

The balance between too much and too little aggression can only be adjusted by each of us if we learn how aggressive we are, what our Internal Aggression Quotient is. Once we know it, we can either strengthen it or lighten it, come on stronger or easier. The end result must be more creative coping.

[CHAPTER THREE]

Using Crutches to Cope with Life

WHEN AN AID BECOMES A PROBLEM

Ten-year-old Peter broke his leg and the doctor put it in a cast and gave him a crutch to walk with. "Just to keep your balance. We don't want you cracking that new cast."

The cast finally came off and the doctor showed Peter and his mother the X-rays. "Beautiful healing. You can give up the crutch now, Pete."

"I'll keep it a day or two till I get used to walking," Peter said. "Is that okay?"

"Why not?" The doctor laughed. "Most of my patients can't wait to get rid of crutches."

But Peter was different. He clung to the crutch beyond the "few days," even a few weeks, and finally his mother, very concerned, took him back to the doctor.

"But you don't need a crutch anymore." The doctor frowned.

"Well, it gives me confidence."

Shaking his head, the doctor said, "Pete, when you break a leg you use a crutch to support your weight till the break heals. Once that happens you must, I repeat *must,* give up the crutch. If you don't, the muscles of your leg will waste away and you'll become a real cripple. Let's look at that leg of yours."

There was, even in the few weeks that Peter had used the crutch, some muscle wasting. Fortunately the doctor scared Peter into abandoning the crutch and the muscles recovered.

A coping crutch is very much like a physical crutch, and should be used for only a limited time. It can act as a psychological support for a damaged ego, but once the damage is repaired the ego must be allowed to support itself. You can waste away psychologically if you keep using the crutch.

Just what are coping crutches?

The businessman's cigar may be one. It can give him enough assurance to face a troublesome client. The swinging single's sports car can be one, too. It shores up his manhood. The young baby's blanket is a crutch, and so is his mother's tranquilizing pill that helps her get through the day. The cigarette her husband lights as soon as he steps off the bus is a crutch and so is the fix the addict takes in the dark alley.

Coping crutches come in a variety of forms, but America's most popular is alcohol. Sally is a good example of someone dependent on this particular crutch. "Why do I need a drink to enjoy a party?" She shrugs. "I guess I could do without it, but wow, when that third martini hits the pit of my stomach and I feel that nice, warm glow take over—it becomes a whole new ball game.

"I'm relaxed, poised, at ease, vivacious—I can go up to absolute strangers and be charming. Hey, listen—how can anyone cope with a cocktail party without cocktails?"

Andy, who likes Sally, but disapproves of her drinking, has his own crutch—Valium.

"I don't need something to turn me on, the way Sally does. I'm turned on all the time. That's my trouble. I'm always hyped up. So I pop a Valium a couple of times a day. It levels me off, takes the edge of hysteria off my work—you don't know the pressures I face at the office, it's unbelievable. A pill gets me through the day and I take another in the evening to relax. What's the big deal? I'm no addict."

The thin line that separates an addict from a confirmed pill popper like Andy is easy to cross. Tranquilizing pills, like alcohol, are rarely considered addictive, but the people who use them as coping crutches never seem to find the right time to give them up.

Although it isn't considered addictive by some doctors, alcohol resembles the "hard drugs" in many ways. These drugs are also used at first as crutches to cope with an overwhelming life situation, but addiction makes the crutch permanent.

MOTHER'S LITTLE HELPER

A surprising number of drug addicts cope with their habit without resorting to crime and many of them are not part of the counterculture. They're valuable members of society, but they're still addicts. They must have their daily fix of hard drugs, but they work in industry and are able to maintain their habits on their salaries and function productively.

Betty Ann is a functional drug addict, too, but she's not hooked on hard drugs that must be bought illegally. She uses prescription drugs to cope with life, but no one labels her a junkie nor harasses her. Betty Ann is a middle-class, middle-aged suburban housewife with four grown children. One's still in college, but the others are married and have children of their own.

Of course, Bud isn't much of a husband. He goes his own way and always did. He has an apartment in town and two women that Betty Ann knows about—and some others that she doesn't. As much as she can, she's accepted her life. When the kids were at home she was involved with them and could blot out her own loneliness. Now that the house is empty and her own life even emptier, she uses Seconal to cope.

"When I had surgery a few years ago," she explains, "I was given a Seconal prescription to tide me over the postoperative stuff—you know, all that pain and depression." She shrugs. "But the pills put everything into perspective. I found I didn't miss the kids so much and Bud—well, it just didn't matter what he thought."

When the prescription ran out, Betty Ann renewed it. When the druggist suggested she get a new one, she switched druggists. Over the years she's been very cunning. By changing doctors and druggists and using all sorts of tricks, she manages to keep a good supply of Seconal and a few other barbiturates.

"They're all harmless," she shrugs, "and they help me cope."

Betty Ann has a friend who uses over-the-counter pills to cope. She doesn't need a prescription to buy Sominex and Compoz. She simply doubles and triples the recommended dosage. The point is, Betty Ann and her friend aren't unusual. The housewife hooked on pills is so common that some years ago a popular song told of the shelter of mother's little helper.

For every pill addict who uses tranquilizers to cope, there's another who uses energizers. These pep you up instead of calming you down. Amphetamines, called "speed" when sold illegally, are in this group.

Allison is hooked on speed, though she doesn't think of it as being hooked. "Like I started it in college when I had this weight problem. I just can't take it off without pills, and then I began using the pills to study, you know, when I had to stay up late. They work great. Now—now I just like what they do to me, the way I feel when I'm on them."

Valium, Seconal, the amphetamines—all of these drugs have a useful place in good medicine. They are valid coping crutches and are prescribed by most physicians. In this country alone there are about twenty-seven million people with cardiovascular disease. Drs. Reiser and Bakst, writing about the psychology of cardiovascular disorders in the *American Handbook of Psychiatry,* stress how difficult it is to cope with the terrifying aspects of this disease, and with the stress responsible for the disease in the first place.

Stress causes changes in the heart and blood vessels, and these changes increase the risk of cardiovascular disease. The disease, in turn, causes additional stress. A vicious circle is set up and if the patient is to cope the circle must be broken.

Tranquilizers can break the circle and act as coping crutches to tide the patient over the crises. The doctor may prescribe them for that period, but the patient can continue to use them until his inner resources begin to waste away.

Methadone, the drug used to help addicts cope with their addiction, has other coping uses as well. I have a friend who is dying of cancer. She's a brave woman and has lived a full, rich life. "I've accepted death," she told me. "What I cannot accept is the pain. It terrifies me, and I can't face the end like that."

When the pain got too intense, she was fortunate enough to receive therapy at the hospital's pain clinic where she was put on Methadone. "I can cope with the cancer now," she said. "With the pain gone, I can manage." Methadone, as a crutch, has allowed her to live the rest of her life with dignity.

THE DOUBLE CRUTCH

Some coping crutches, like alcohol and drugs, are potentially dangerous. Others, like cigarettes, are double coping crutches. On the one hand, the nicotine in cigarettes stimulates and relaxes us at the same time to help us deal with tension. However, the very act of smoking is a coping crutch. We first learn to smoke so that we may appear cool and at ease in tight situations. It gives us something to do with our hands. It acts as a body language device to signal any number of messages—maturity, disdain, sexual interest. At a cocktail party, a cigarette helps us handle the general awkwardness of standing around, doing nothing. In a business conference, it puts us at ease, lets us appear assured.

Once we accept the concept of coping crutches, we can examine our lives and discover just how many crutches we use. Possessions, alcohol, drugs, cigarettes are all obvious ones. But there are others. Food is often used as a coping crutch. Humans are tremendously concerned with it. From earliest times, man hunted desperately for food. Primitive man's entire life was devoted to it. Women constantly gathered seeds, fruit, nuts, and grains while men hunted or fished. Famine waited in the wings to step out the moment the search slackened.

Somewhere along the line a direct connection was made between food and love. Some parents confuse the two and stuff their children as an act of love. An adult reared with the equation food equals love will often turn to food to cope with a lack of love, or with loneliness or unhappiness. The food provides oral satisfaction and deeper psychological satisfaction.

Patricia heads straight for the ice cream store at the first sign of stress. "Why?" she asks, plunging into a double sundae with whipped cream and nuts, "I guess because the sweets are a comfort. Look, when I had a disappointment as a kid, my mother was always right on target with 'Sit down. Have a piece of cake and some milk—you'll feel better. You failed a course? Eat. You broke up with the boyfriend? Eat. You lost your job? Eat, eat, eat!'

"When I broke up with Harry, my husband, I went

on an eating binge for a week and gained ten pounds—ten pounds in one week!"

The other side of the coin is Jesse. She has anorexia nervosa, that sad illness where rebellion against her parents is tied up with an aversion to food. "I'm just not able to eat," she protests. "It's not that I don't want to—I can't. I gag on the food." But the truth is Jesse uses her inability to eat as a crutch to cope with the anger and hostility she feels for her parents.

"But if she admitted this now, it would destroy her," her psychiatrist says. "We have to first bring her to the point where she can admit it to herself, and then choose another weapon besides starvation—if she survives that long."

Most coping crutches are material things, but some are conditions. Illness can be a coping crutch. When children are sick they receive an additional dose of attention, affection, or love from their parents. How easy it is to turn it around and look for attention, affection, and love by becoming ill.

Usually the coper isn't aware that he's using illness as a crutch to get what he wants. His illness is real to him, no matter what caused it. Sometimes the illness is deliberately faked to cope with a need for sympathy, or it may be stretched out as long as possible to cope with loneliness. The hypochondriac is usually starved for affection or attention.

As with most coping crutches, a little phony illness to get attention may not be all bad. Some children need to stay home from school occasionally to be fussed over in a sick bed. A touch of the "vapors" can give them the strength to cope with school the next day. But an adult shouldn't need this type of crutch. For one thing, it inevitably puts too big a strain on the person who must cope with the invalid.

Sleep is another common crutch for coping with an unhappy situation. It does away with the need to cope.

You can't cope when you're asleep, so if something is too difficult to handle, doze off. How common is this escape? Think of all the husbands who doze off in the evening rather than face the family problems, the students who retreat to sleep in the face of overwhelming homework, and the wives or husbands who fall asleep quickly to avoid sex.

THE ODD COUPLE

A crutch can also be another human being. Leona uses Charlie to cope with loneliness. At thirty-four, still single and attractive, Leona knows that Charlie is no good for her. They've been seeing each other, on and off, for the past ten years, and each time they break up violently.

Once Charlie locked Leona out of his apartment at three in the morning, and she walked the streets for hours, barefoot and half hysterical.

Another time the neighbors had to call the police to break up a furious battle between them. Each time they split, Leona swears it's the end. And yet, as if repeating a pattern beyond her control, she'll get back together with Charlie before the year is up.

"I can't help myself," Leona explains. "I need Charlie. I don't love him—God knows—it's nearer hate. I pick at him like a carrion bird at an old carcass, and yet—" Biting her lip, she shakes her head. "When I get terribly lonely and depressed, when my room closes in and the job gets so hateful I could scream, I begin to think of Charlie again. Once I'm with him again I'm able to take all the shit life hands out—it's only Charlie who gets harder and harder to take. I don't understand it myself."

But it's not hard to understand. Leona leans on Charlie. He's the crutch she needs to carry her over her neurotic depressions. She can't live with him for any length of time, and she knows it. If she could she'd probably marry him, not out of love but out of need, because she can only cope with life when Charlie's there.

And Charlie? "I guess I love Leona. If I didn't I'd have killed her long ago. Sure I take her back, even when I know it's wrong. Why? Because I don't think she can make it without me."

In a way Charlie is right, but he needs her, too. Each is the other's private hell. When Leona breaks away it's not because she's strong enough to do without him, but because she can't do without him.

Often a destructive element enters the relationship when one person uses another to cope with life. Nobody likes to be used, and in retaliation will often undermine the one he supports. Charlie will tear Leona down and destroy her self-confidence even while he claims he loves her.

And yet we all start life depending on another person. We cling to our mother, and later to our father. But we move away when we are able to. One day at the beach I smiled at a toddler, and he quickly moved back to the shelter of his father's legs, grabbing them with one hand. Then he looked up at me with serious eyes. When I smiled again, he smiled back—from the safety of his father's legs. He could cope as long as he had his father for support.

Earlier in the book we saw how Sam was able to cope with his accident as long as he had his mother for support. My toddler at the beach eventually moved away from his father to show me a toy he had, just as Sam moved away from his mother when he was strong enough.

We can use other people as crutches in a good sense, even on a continuing basis. In a good marriage a husband will use his wife to help him cope with life, just as she uses him, but neither need be diminished by the process. If both give as well as get there will be a successful balance.

In the same way a boss uses an employee to cope with the business world, but the employee gets as he gives and the relationship is mutually beneficial. If it's bad, the business suffers. There may be a strike, a firing—or any of a dozen things to destroy the imbalance.

THE ANTI-LONELINESS BOX

There are other coping crutches that we tend to overlook, and television is one. Old people, lonely people, cope with isolation and despair by watching television. I know of one woman in her eighties with no family and very few friends who has built a set of substitute friends and relations in the TV world. To her Johnny Carson is Johnny, and she knows every detail of his life and cherishes all the *in* jokes about him. She writes him letters and knits him scarves. He's a part of her life, a bulwark against loneliness.

She has other *friends,* too, and she'll tell anecdotes about Lucy and Merv and Mike. They're real people to her, sharing her life and helping her deal with all the endless, empty hours.

I've heard middle-class people complain about the number of TV aerials in ghetto neighborhoods, but ghetto kids cope with desperation by watching the glowing, TV dream world, and so do ghetto adults.

Mothers in all levels of society use television to cope with their children. One harassed mother of three told me she never watches it herself. "Who has time? But God, what a beautiful baby-sitter it is. I plant the kids in front of it, and they sit there mesmerized whether it's a good program or bad. At least it gives me some time to get my work done."

And of course there are the shut-ins, the invalids

who find some escape in the magic box, and the inarticulate people who have nothing to say to each other, but who turn on the TV with relief and let it talk for them. I know a bright, childless couple who keep their set on constantly, even when they entertain. "It's company," is the best way they can explain it. "It fills the house."

COPING CRUTCHES

A crutch is used to help someone walk until he can help himself, and in the same way a coping crutch helps us deal with life until our coping strengths or tools are well developed. But holding on to a crutch beyond the point where we need it can be a disabling thing. Our own. It is also important to recognize the *things* we use strengths can fail to develop.

And yet a crutch can be useful. The important point is knowing when to discard it and move forward on your own. It is also important to recognize the *things* we use as crutches—alcohol, drugs, food, and even other people.

Once we are aware that these are crutches, we can think in terms of using them only until we can stand on our own feet. Then we can change our relationship to them. Drink can become a pleasant relaxant, drugs a medical help, food something to nourish us, and we can come to love and respect other people instead of using them to support ourselves.

[CHAPTER FOUR]

Flexibility: How to Change Horses in Midstream

ON BEING A TYCOON

Rodney Allen is a successful businessman, the kind newspapers like to call a tycoon. "There are plenty of men richer than I am," he told a reporter who interviewed him. "But I'm up there, and I've made it all the hard way. I clawed my way up the corporate ladder of an ad agency, and then I moved over to the client we served. I've gone straight up since then."

When the reporter asked him how he had done it, what one factor had contributed most to his success, he smiled and shook his head. "I'll tell you, and you'd better believe it. I was never afraid to change horses in midstream."

Pressed, he explained himself. "If I had a pet idea and it wasn't working out, I'd step back and take another look at it, try and see it from another angle, to find out if it was really as good as I thought it was.

"You know, when you like an idea—or a person, for that matter—it's hard to see any flaws or faults. I would deliberately look for the flaws and search out the faults. If I found them and realized the idea was no good, then I gave it up right away and I'd try something else."

"And with people?" the reporter asked.

Allen shrugged. "Call it ruthless if you want to. I

call it realistic. When a man didn't work out I abandoned him. I let him go. But that's not the point. What really matters is that I never let myself become rigid. You want one word to sum it up? Flexibility. That's the key."

Allen was right. Of all the skills we develop to cope with life, flexibility is one of the most important. Just what is flexibility? In a nutshell, it's *an awareness of alternative solutions as well as the ability to discard one solution if it doesn't work and select another.*

Put this way, it seems so logical and obvious that there should be no need to think about it twice. A well-built computer can respond to a problem flexibly and choose the solution most likely to work. However, for better or worse, men are not computers. As part of the human condition, they often have a built-in rigidity. People like to do things the way they've always done them. Nobody wants to discard an idea if they've invested some time in it.

THE FLEXIBLE MAN

For many of us, the idea of flexibility is too closely tied to vacillating. We think it goes hand in hand with an inability to make up our minds. We look at a flexible man as a weak one. If he can't get what he wants he takes second best.

But is this a weakness? Or is it simply that the flexible man doesn't limit himself? If necessary, he's ready to switch goals if he can't get the one he wants. He doesn't try to reach the top of Everest just because it's there. While he laces up his climbing boots he asks how important it is to get to the top, and if the risks are too great, he settles for a point he can reach.

Flexibility, then, is not exactly the obvious approach it seems at first glance. It requires a particular kind of philosophy to be truly flexible. The flexible man is continually reevaluating his goals. He's constantly questioning himself about the importance of these goals. Above all, he's able to fight the clichés and symbols of our culture—in short, he knows how to test reality at every step.

In doing this, does he lose too much? Is he risking his sense of individuality? Must he give up the American Dream?

We've been taught that if we set our sights on a goal and go after it, we'll succeed. After all, this is the land of success. All it wants is hard work and determination, and someday one of us will be president—if not of the nation, then at least of General Motors.

Must we lose this dream if we adopt a flexible approach to life? Of course we must, but we must also realize that it is only a dream. We must understand the odds against achieving it. We have to answer honestly, how realistic is our goal?

SHIFTING GEARS

In the play *Death of a Salesman,* Arthur Miller showed a man destroyed because the American Dream didn't work out for him. Miller's play was popular because the dream hadn't worked for an entire generation. Logic tells us that it can only work for a handful. Our society is a pyramid with a vast base supporting a small top, and there's very limited room at the top.

If we don't make it up there, should we take it as a proof of personal inadequacy—as Miller's salesman did—or should we attack the system and say, "Everything was stacked against me"? Either way leads to bitterness.

It's much more logical to set a realistic goal at the beginning, but logic often takes second place when it comes to understanding our own capabilities and limits. The flexible man sets his goals, but if the odds against him are too high, he shifts to the next realistic goal—but he shifts without a sense of failure.

A recent article in *New York* Magazine illustrates this point very clearly. Headlined "Ten Survivors of the Wall Street Crash," it consists of mini-interviews with ten men who were in the brokerage business on Wall Street until the crash. Each faced the end of his career. How did he cope?

Eight applied the principle of flexibility. They examined all their other options, then got out of the brokerage business and into something else. One became a landscape gardener. Another opened a bicycle shop; still another a delicatessen. One became a Hollywood producer and one made a fortune when the bull market disappeared by switching to beef. He opened a restaurant called the Bum Steer. One is entering medical school, another is in real estate, and the eighth is in carpets.

Two of the ten remained in the stock market in different jobs at reduced salaries.

The interesting thing is that none of the eight who took his second choice regrets what he's done. None looks on it as copping out or giving up. Their comments are revealing:

"It makes a lot of sense . . ."

"I'm getting to know my wife and kids better."

"I'm free to do whatever I want."

"How much money I make is secondary."

These are satisfied men. They were all on the main road to success and they hit a road block. Eight shifted gears and took a side road. You shift gears in life as you do in a car. Only a fool would drive in high on a steep mountain road. The sensible man shifts down to the gear that will let the car make it with no strain.

TESTING YOUR FLEXIBILITY

There is another aspect to flexibility: the search for alternative solutions to a problem. Again it's a matter of avoiding rigidity. If the flexible man must get to

Washington from New York and the airport is snowed in, he tries for a ticket on the Metroliner. If that isn't running, he calls the bus terminal or he rents a car and drives. Instead of giving up on his ultimate goal, he searches for a workable alternative to reach that goal.

Our first step toward any goal is to test the reality of the goal. Can we reach it?

Our second step is to test our motivation. Do we want to get there enough to warrant the attempt?

If both answers are *yes,* then we should take the third step and discover all the different routes to our goal. Here are three small problems that will help you to understand your own flexibility or rigidity. Each one concerns a rigid person, or a person who lives by rigid standards. In each case they've boxed themselves into a dead end, and yet each problem can be solved by a flexible approach. Consider each one and list all the possible approaches that occur to you.

If you see no way out, you're looking at the world too rigidly.

If you can find five answers, you're extremely flexible. Two or three are good—but no matter how many you find, only one is necessary to cope.

Clock yourself as you think the problem through. Again, the faster a solution comes to mind, the more flexible you are.

The Case of the Fresh Kid

Nine-year-old Lenny's mother is upset. He's been sent home from school for being fresh and talking back to the teacher. This has happened before and his mother put down some very strict rules. She warned him that if he got into trouble with his teacher again he'd have to stay in the house for the entire weekend. Now she realizes that this is also going to tie her up for the weekend—and also, no nine-year-old should be punished that severely.

Yet she's made it a rule to be consistent with Lenny, and she feels she just can't go back on her word.

The Case of the Hot-Shot Salesman

Al Myles is executive vice-president in charge of sales at Multiple Data Associates, an international firm with branches all over the world. Lee Gold is one of MDA's top salesmen and troubleshooters, and recently he approached Al for a sizeable raise.

Al thinks Lee deserves it. He hates to think of what the department would be without him, but he has some rigid rules linking raises to seniority. He's never broken the rules because he knows a corporation must be consistent to its employees—and Lee hasn't nearly enough seniority for the money he wants.

But he also knows that Lee is top-notch, and any number of competing firms are ready to pirate him away.

The Case of the Meaningful Relationship

Alicia has been living with Justin for almost a year. She feels they have a heavy thing going and a beautiful commitment to each other, but she's not ready for marriage. Maybe she never will be. She was married once and it was so awful she won't even talk about it.

Justin has always wanted to marry her, but he's taken what he feels is second best—living together. Now his folks are coming to town and they want to stay with him. They don't know about Alicia, and they're very old-fashioned. "Square, but I love them," Justin says. "No way could I tell them what's going on. Why don't we get married?"

"I've told you how I feel. That's it. Period!"

"Well, I'm telling you," Justin answers angrily. "We've got a month to make a decision."

"Like what?"

"Like we get married or we split."

Alicia looks at him levelly for a long minute, then says, "I won't be blackmailed."

But later, to her dismay, she realizes how much she wants Justin. She can't marry him, but she doesn't want to lose him.

THE OAK AND THE REED

There's an old fable about an oak tree and a reed. The oak tree would tease the swaying reed. "Look at me," he'd say pompously, "I never bend."

Then a furious windstorm toppled the oak. The reed, as usual, bent before the wind and afterwards looked down at the fallen oak sadly and said, "You should have learned to bend like me."

In truth, few things in nature are that rigid. Flexibility is a built-in function of matter, and of life, too—or it should be. We learn flexibility at an early age. The baby who accepts a bottle instead of a breast is using a flexible approach, but whether the flexibility grows or withers depends very much on the child's parents.

When Lillian and Ann were toddlers, they were both bright, alert little girls. However, Lillian drove her mother to distraction while Ann and her mother got along very well. The credit went to Ann's mother because of the way she parlayed Ann's inherent flexibility into pleasant management, and Lillian's mother was to blame for a lot of her stubbornness.

For example, one afternoon when her mother was preparing dinner, Lillian asked, "Can I cook on the gas stove like you?"

"Absolutely not!" Lillian's mother told her, and tried to explain the dangers of an open flame. Lillian begged and coaxed, and the usual family hassle began.

When Ann asked the same question, her mother smiled agreeably. "That's a wonderful idea. Why don't you cook the dessert? You can make instant pudding all by yourself and we'll have it for supper."

Ann was offered an alternative that included the fun of cooking, but eliminated the danger of an open flame. She accepted it happily because it had a built-in reward. *We'll have it for supper.*

When Lillian's mother wanted her to do something, she told her to do it. "I don't believe in permissiveness. A child must know what she has to do. There have to be rules," she'd insist, and she'd tell Lillian, "You can't go out and play if you don't pick up your toys."

Ann's mother approached the same problem from a slightly different angle. "You can go out and play," she assured Ann, "right after you pick up your toys."

"I can go out and play," Ann would chant as she tidied up. But Lillian would argue and pout and cry until, "You can't go out at all!" would settle the argument.

"I'm not permissive," Ann's mother explained. "I have rules, too. I simply present Ann with reasonable alternatives. She knows what she wants. I allow her to get what she wants if she does what I want."

By the time they were teen-agers, Ann and Lillian had completely different approaches to life. Lillian had locked herself into a pattern of rigidity as unbending as the oak tree. There was no suggestion her mother could make that wasn't fought bitterly and stubbornly.

It was that way with her friends, too. "You can't argue with Lil," they'd say. "When she latches on to an idea, that's it!"

And even more important, Lillian couldn't handle defeat. During college she moved in with a man her mother didn't like. There was a heavy family row, but Lillian held firm. When the young man walked out on her six months later she was devastated. She didn't date again for over a year, and refused to see her parents for any reason during that time.

Ann went through a similar love affair—or almost similar. Before she moved in with the boy her mother sat down with her. "I know you think you love Archie, and maybe you do. You know that better than I do. But I know you, and I've seen a lot of Archie recently, and a lot of the two of you together.

"Archie's a good person in many ways, but I honestly have to tell you that I don't think he's right for you. Maybe you can work it out, but I don't think so. What do you think?"

Ann was hurt and didn't want to discuss it. For a week she avoided her mother, and then she came home one afternoon and told her, "You were right. I didn't want to believe you, but I thought it all over carefully, and last night Archie and I had a long rap session. It's all finished. We parted friends, but both of us realized it wouldn't work. Thanks, Mom."

"I haven't got the kind of daughter who automatically rejects what I say," Ann's mother explained later. "Sure, she wants to do things her own way, and she usually does. Sometimes she's right, and sometimes she finds out later that she did the wrong thing. But we all make mistakes and learn from them. It's only when the results will be very serious that I step in and offer advice. I can do it because I've never dictated to her. I've always given her choices. When I take sides, she knows I have a damned good reason!"

SEXUAL FLEXIBILITY

The need for flexibility doesn't diminish, no matter how old we get. Dr. Harold Lief, director of the Marriage Council of Philadelphia, told a recent symposium on sexuality and the aging process about an elderly couple with a sad problem that was all too common in their age group.

The sixty-five-year-old husband was impotent, and because of it he was afraid to touch his wife, to embrace her or kiss her. He thought that if he did, the embrace or kiss might become sexual and lead to an attempt at intercourse—an attempt he knew would fail.

Rather than risk the sexual failure, he settled for no contact at all. His wife, five years younger, hesitated to show too much affection to him for the same reason. She loved him so much that she dreaded making him feel inadequate. She never touched him, but kept her distance even though kissing and caressing were more important to her at this point in life than the act of intercourse.

Commenting on these lonely people, Dr. Lief condemned "Freudian rigidity that made all of us think the only mature kind of sexuality is coital and all other aspects of sex are infantile and immature."

If they had been more flexible, he suggested, these two could have settled for intimate touching instead of sex, and they would have been happy with that substitution.

It is interesting, as a follow-up to the story, to know that under the guidance of the Marriage Council the two older people finally settled for physical contact and forgot their worries about sexual intercourse.

Once they made this decision, they were able to relax and enjoy their intimacy. With the relaxation, the husband's tension disappeared and to his amazement so did his impotence. Ironically, they were led back to the sexual intercourse they had both decided to give up.

There is nothing surprising about this because in essence it is the technique that sex researchers Masters and Johnson have used so successfully to treat impotence. In most cases, impotence is a mental, not a physical problem. Something—drink, exhaustion, nervousness—causes impotence one time. Most men have these minor troubles with impotence and shrug them off. A night later, or a week later they're fine. But sometimes if they're particularly vulnerable and insecure they begin to worry about it happening again. The worry itself can lead to another bout of impotence, and this can start a vicious circle of worry/failure/worry/failure.

Masters and Johnson teach men to cope with this impotence by using flexibility. They substitute another type of sexuality, caressing and lovemaking without intercourse. With the anxiety to perform removed, the men find that the ability to have intercourse returns.

USING FLEXIBILITY CREATIVELY

The flexible man is a creative coper, and he's the one who has sense enough to recognize a dead end when he is in one and to search for a workable alternative. He is able to shift gears or change his approach when things aren't working out properly. He must be constantly aware of reality, and this awareness helps him realize just how much he can achieve in any coping situation. It not only tells him when to stop trying, but also when to keep trying, when he has a realistic chance of success.

A deeper recognition of flexibility as a coping tool allows you to use it to sway other people. Parents, willing to use a little flexibility, can move their children in almost any direction. Teachers can influence pupils, and supervisors can reach the people under them. The key, of course, is to abolish rigidity. Reexamine your motives, your goals, your procedures, and do it at crucial intervals. Each time decide how deeply you're locked into the wrong path—or committed to the right one.

[CHAPTER FIVE]

Learning the Five Faces of Reason

Most of us use reason to deal with life, but few of us can explain reason, define it, or truly understand it. Psychologists, who know its value in coping, have compared it to a pentagon. Each side of the pentagon stands for one of the five functions of reason: ambiguity, objectivity, discrimination, detachment, and logic.

THE MAN WHO COULDN'T SEE GRAY

To understand how we can use reason as a coping tool, we should examine each of its five sides separately, then take a look at how the entire pentagon works. First, consider ambiguity, the ability to see things in terms of gray instead of black and white. Many of us do this automatically, but many of us can't.

Take Sheldon, who was a nonambiguous man. He had only two ways of looking at life. Everything was either good or bad, right or wrong, pleasant or unpleasant —either/or. For Sheldon there was nothing in between. Seeing the world this way, he found it very difficult to cope.

"His biggest trouble is keeping a job," his wife complained. "With Sheldon, everyone is either a good guy or a bad guy. The good guys can do no wrong, and the bad guys can do no right. With that kind of attitude, how can anything work out?"

It was bad enough that Sheldon's lack of ambiguity interfered with his marriage and job. It was very sad that it also influenced the way he saw his children. They were good or bad. If Jimmy talked back, he was a bad kid headed for trouble. There weren't any excuses. If little Al played with an erector set instead of doing his arithmetic, he was being naughty—never mind the complex numbers and angles he learned from the toy.

When Sally, his oldest girl, married a man without a job, Sheldon blew his stack. "Don't think I'm going to pretend I like it. It'll ruin her life. A boy who hasn't got a job? He's a bum!"

In spite of his wife's pleading, he refused to be anything but civil, and after some bitter arguments Sally cut herself off from the family completely. She was happy in her marriage even though they didn't have a cent. Eventually her husband found some odd jobs with a housebuilder. He and Sally were broke most of the time, but they didn't care. They lived the way they wanted to.

But Sheldon had locked himself out of their life. He just couldn't cope with the idea that someone who didn't play by his rules was still in the game.

Now most of us aren't like Sheldon. We know that life consists of shades of gray, and yet the world is still presented to us in black and white. Turn on your TV or pick up your local newspaper and you read about the rich and the poor, the perpetrators and the cops, the beautiful people and the ugly, the good guys and the bad guys.

A true sense of ambiguity would help us see all the people in between, and it would also allow us to look at what happens from many different viewpoints. It would help us to question life and perhaps force us to grow a bit and become more tolerant and understanding of others.

It's unfortunate that so many teachers in our schools fail to look at their students ambiguously. By the end of the first few grades most children have been marked down as smart or dumb. But intelligence is never an either/or attribute. Some of the smartest people can do very stupid things, and some pretty stupid people are very shrewd.

Before Kinsey dredged up some of our far-out sexual habits, everyone was either straight or gay. Since Kinsey, we've found a lot of bisexuals coming out of the closets—and we've become aware of all the variations in between the homosexual and the heterosexual.

MIRROR, MIRROR ON THE WALL

Objectivity is the second side of the pentagon of reason. Objectivity is a mirror that doubles your length of focus and lets you take a good, hard look at what you're doing, what you are, and what you want.

John often found it hard to take an objective view of what his son Peter did. When Peter crumpled the front end of the family car in a minor traffic accident, John was furious.

"At least I didn't total it!" Peter protested.

"Big deal. Am I supposed to give you a medal for that?"

"But it's only the hood, Dad. I stopped at the garage on the way home, and they can fix it for two hundred and fifty bucks."

"Sure, and I've got a hundred deductible. You kids think I'm made of money!" John shouted.

"I said I'd pay for it."

"Damn right you will. Haven't you any sense of responsibility?" And then John really laced into his son and ended the tirade by grounding him indefinitely.

Peter took it, but left the room sullenly.

When John had calmed down, his wife said, "I really don't see why you were so hard on Pete."

"Don't you? My God, he could have been killed—aside from what he did to the car."

"It was an accident, John. He didn't do it deliberately, and he's not a reckless kid. You know that."

Later, alone in his study, John thought over what his wife had said. It was true. He had been outraged out of all proportion to what had happened. Fortunately, he was a flexible man. He hadn't been at all objective in his first reaction, but now, thinking it over, he could step back and size up the situation.

A lot of his anger, he realized, was really guilt. He was the one who gave Peter the keys to the car, and Peter was barely seventeen. How would he have felt if the accident had been serious? He began to realize that he had acted on a purely emotional level. Grounding Peter indefinitely was unfair.

Being the man he was, John went upstairs and knocked on Peter's door. "Can I come in?"

"I'd rather be alone." Peter's voice was thick.

Ignoring his protests, John went in and sat on his son's bed. "Pete, I know you're not a reckless kid. We all make mistakes. I made one when I bawled you out—maybe you made one when you crumpled the front end. It probably wasn't your fault. At least you weren't hurt, and that's what really matters to me."

Peter looked at him searchingly, then grinned with relief. "Dad, I truly am sorry!"

John gave him a quick hug. "Me, too."

John had the good luck to cope with the same situation twice. First he coped the wrong way. Then, using objectivity, he took the right way. Of course, there are any number of wrong and right ways of coping with any incident. The key to a right way is that touch of objectivity, the ability to stand back for a moment and assess the situation, to look into that special mirror and see what you're really up to.

In John's case, after his wife pointed out his mistake, he was able to separate his emotional from his intellectual reaction and then move in and handle the problem. This is no easy trick, and men like John—who can do it every day in the business world—find it hard to be objective at home with their children, wives, or parents. Of course the emotional involvement is much closer in a family than in a business deal, and emotion darkens the mirror of objectivity.

A businessman can't be emotional, or lose his temper, when he's making an important decision. Not if he wishes to get ahead. But as objective as businessmen must be, they also have to learn to play the game of "non-objectivity." When an objective evaluation of the situation indicates that a show of anger will work to his advantage, losing his temper becomes a calculated ploy for coping.

Losing your temper at a critical time is one aspect of controlled objectivity—another is the pretense that your emotion rules your judgment. This can lead to a successful disarming of your opponent in the business arena.

"I like you . . . I'm going to give you a great deal . . . I couldn't sleep nights if I cheated you . . . My word is as good as my bond . . ."

Or it can lead to the disarming of the consumer. "Trust us as a corporation . . . You can depend on us . . . You can rely on our product . . ."

In a negative way, all these disclaimers admit the importance of objectivity. They do it by using an emotional appeal to confuse intellectual judgment. Once this is accomplished, the business opponent or the consumer finds it difficult to cope.

A shrewd businessman discounts emotional disclaimers and simply does not trust the man he deals with. He protects himself with legal contracts and agreements. In this way he effectively separates emotion from reason and he can look at any deal objectively. He can examine the product or service on its own merits, not on unproven claims.

The smart consumer, often ill-equipped to cope

objectively with the manufacturer or seller, turns to objective crutches—consumer reports and ratings or government analyses.

The manufacturer or seller relies on advertising to prevent consumer objectivity. The skilled advertising agency links an emotional appeal to the product; a beautiful woman to a car, an athletic man to a cigarette, a famous personality to a whisky—all in an attempt to prevent objectivity.

THE THIRD SIDE OF REASON

Once we develop a sense of ambiguity and the ability to be objective, we are ready to learn the third side of reason's pentagon: discrimination. It's one thing to realize that the world exists in shades of gray. It's quite another thing to evaluate the shades and discriminate among them. If you have only two choices, your decision will be much simpler than if you have ten.

I had a young friend, Mel, who was completely unable to cope with his parents until he learned discrimination, and he couldn't learn that until he developed a sense of ambiguity and gained some objectivity.

When I first met him he felt there was no possible way he could talk to his parents. "They call it a generation gap," he confided, "but it's more than that. It's like they're earthmen and I'm a Martian. We can't communicate. I wouldn't mind that so much, but put us in the same room, each of us doing his own thing, and in ten minutes it's total disaster. The only way I'm gonna survive is I cut out of here—but if I do, they'll bring me back. I'm only sixteen."

There was no ambiguity in the way Mel saw his situation. He felt he had two possibilities: stay at home and tear himself and his parents apart, or run away and buy himself a mess of trouble. Either way was disaster.

"It's just a case of which is worse," he said gloomily. "Which will hurt my parents least, because, damn it, I love them! That's the hell of it."

I liked Mel too much to see him tormented like this, and taking off from that first indication of ambiguity—I love them—I began to sound him out on the various shades of gray in the situation. It wasn't quite as black and white as he saw it. Granted he couldn't live with his parents the way things were. Were there any alternatives?

"Well, sure. There's boarding school. Dad says he can afford it. He even suggested it once, but I told him it's trading one prison for another. Maybe I didn't mean it. I wanted to hurt him then."

"But you did talk to him. So you can communicate. You're not quite a Martian."

"We used hand signals." He laughed. "Okay. If I try hard enough we can talk."

There was another alternative. Try hard enough to talk things out. Get his father to understand what he wanted out of life—if he understood it himself. As we talked, more alternatives opened up. He loved his grandmother and got along with her. She wanted him to come and live at her house, and his mother had agreed. His mother had also suggested some therapy for the entire family to help them get together. The list grew, and the black-and-white situation took on tones of gray.

Mel was clever and perceptive. In the weeks that followed, as he began to see and understand the possible alternatives, he was able to step back and view the situation objectively, to separate his emotions from what was best for his parents and himself.

Leaving home, he realized, was the way he would hurt them most. When he felt that was the only answer he had been motivated by a desire to punish them, but at the same time he didn't really want to hurt them. He wanted their love too much, and he himself loved them.

As his motivations began to fall into place, he was

able to use discrimination to evaluate each choice and to understand which would be best for the family as a whole.

When I saw him a year later, he had come a long way. "Hell, we haven't solved all our problems, but we talk to each other now. I'm living at home and I'm not hating it. I give a little here and tighten up there, and they bend with me, It's funny. They haven't changed, really. But now I can cope with them. The hardest thing is when I have to decide whether or not to do something."

"What do you mean?"

"Well, it's hard to explain, but like when my grandfather died a few months ago. I went to the funeral and then Mom wanted me to write Gran a letter. That was the kind of thing we used to get into real hassles about. Hell, what can you write at a time like that? I know how she loved Grandpa, and I love her—maybe more than I love my own parents. What kind of sentimental crap could I write?"

"How did you handle it?"

"Oh, in the end I wrote, and it was the right thing to do. I could tell by Gran's reaction. Then I understood how much my letter meant to her. But you know why I decided to write?"

"Why?"

"Not because of what Mom said. I just asked myself, what's the hardest thing to do? The answer was writing the letter. So I did it. I'm beginning to realize that when a thing feels real hard to do, it's—well, kind of like my duty to do it."

DETACHMENT AND WITHDRAWAL—THE POSITIVE AND THE NEGATIVE

What Mel had discovered was the fourth side of the pentagon—detachment. The trick of assessing a situation by separating your emotions from your intellect, *what you want to do* from *what is best for you to do.*

The difference between detachment and objectivity is a subtle one. Remember they are both sides of the same pentagon, but the sides are set at a slightly different angle. The man who uses detachment to cope with a problem separates the problem from the things that trouble him—inside things and outside. He won't allow cold, poverty, family demands, or financial needs to spoil his judgment. Neither will he be influenced by hunger, thirst, or sex.

It's a curious thing that the need for sex is so often used as an excuse for a failure to cope. We think of rape as the action of a man who cannot cope, and in a sense we see all male sexuality as so consuming an appetite that men cannot use detachment to cope with it.

Yet one of the most primitive methods of birth control is withdrawal before ejaculation, and this requires the most discriminating detachment at the height of the sexual act. The fact that it has been used throughout the world proves that not even the powerful sex drive is immune to reason.

Some sides of reason's pentagon are easily confused with their negative opposites. Detachment has its opposite side, too. Take the case of Sam, for example. He is shy and introverted but handsome and intelligent and successful in his own small business. He's the delight of any hostess because he's an available, single man. However, he can drive a hostess wild because he reacts to a party by picking up a magazine and settling down in a corner.

Sam doesn't use detachment to cope with his social awkwardness. He withdraws from the group and copes by not coping. It allows Sam to get through the evening, but it does nothing to help him cope with the next party—unless he pulls the magazine-in-the-corner bit again.

Well, if it gets Sam through the party, why shouldn't he use it? Isn't that what coping is all about? Not quite.

The trouble is that Sam's technique is used only because he feels inadequate. He'd really like to be cool about the whole situation. He'd like to move in on some of the women at the party and sound off on politics and literature—he knows a lot about both and has some far-out theories.

What keeps him from making the effort? Not choice, but a fear of being put down. Suppose the women ignore him, or he makes a fool of himself, or he's humiliated. It's better not to try at all. Why take a chance?

But taking a chance is at the very heart of coping. If Sam could separate his emotions, his feeling of inadequacy, his fear of being rebuffed, from the reality of the situation—his own intelligence and a possible evening of fun—then he'd be able to cope with the party. He could use detachment to realize that he was no more awkward than the other guests, and probably not as dull. It's a shame that Sam, a reasoning man, can't use reason to cope.

Sam, like many of us, is a coping cripple, and uses the crutch of withdrawal to get along. The fact that he goes to the party shows that deep down he wants to cope. He wants to reach the point where he can throw away the crutch and be the cool, successful man of his fantasy.

LOGIC, THE AMPLIFIER OF REASON

Logic is the final coping skill that finishes the pentagon. Without it, the other four sides are incomplete. We can use the other sides singly, or in combination, to cope, and they will help us, but we can cope far better when the entire pentagon is available.

Think of what the pentagon would look like if it were crystal and only four sides were polished. It would gleam, but polish the fifth side and the gleam would be reflected with startling brilliance. It wouldn't be one-fifth brighter but five times as bright.

Use logic to amplify the other four parts of reason, and you have more than a better coper. You have a creative coper.

Logic, in a coping sense, is simply the ability to evaluate the different courses of action, to decide which are good for you and which are bad, which are safe and which are dangerous. It is linked to discrimination because we can use logic to select the right thing to do only when we can discriminate among all the available options.

Mel learned first to discriminate and then to detach himself, emotionally, from all the choices that were open. But he couldn't make a choice until he approached every situation logically and understood which was best for him.

Just as withdrawal is the negative image of detachment, rationalization is the negative image of logic. We cannot analyze any situation logically until we eliminate rationalization, *the excuse we use to select the convenient instead of the best solution.*

Sometimes the rationalization is simple to spot. "The extra drink at lunch will calm my nerves and I'll be better with the client . . . If we don't have sex on our first date he won't ask me out again . . . I might as well have the ice cream. It's easier to start a diet on Monday . . . Why not pick this up from the counter? Everyone shoplifts . . . Why give up smoking? I'll probably pick up another habit just as bad . . ." And so it goes.

Sometimes the rationalization that clouds a logical approach is much subtler, at least to the person who uses it. Many of us aren't even aware that we are using it. Mary wasn't. She had been going with Jim for two years, and he wanted to marry her.

"And I'm ready for marriage," she told her best friend. "Overready. I'm close to thirty—on the wrong side."

"Do you love him?"

"I think so." She chewed her lip.

Her friend stubbed out her cigarette. She had been married for five years and considered herself knowledgeable. "The difference between I think and I do gets less after marriage."

"Well, one problem is, Jim comes from a different background."

"So?"

"He thinks marriage is for keeps," Mary said, and added quickly, "So do I, but I don't want to make a mistake I can't change."

"That's wise."

She hesitated. "Jim and his brother were raised by two maiden aunts. It was a pretty religious home."

"Is that so bad?"

Mary sighed. "Well, I'm not a kid and Jim wasn't my first. When we started having sex, it was all right. Not great, but adequate."

Her friend didn't say anything, and Mary went on slowly. "It's become less frequent, and now Jim has trouble making love. He says sex doesn't interest him that much, and it's not the be-all and the end-all of a marriage." At her friend's troubled look, she went on quickly. "Well, he's right. Jim loves me and he needs me—he really does!"

"Do you want to know what I think?"

Mary shook her head. "No. Just let me talk it out. Last night we went out with Jim's brother and his wife and while we were talking in the ladies' room she said, kind of bitterly, that she wanted a baby because maybe that way she'd get a little love out of him. He just stopped having sex with her after they were married." Mary was quiet then.

Finally her friend burst out. "Hell, you've always had your head on straight. What are you getting into?"

"He needs me and I think I can help him," Mary said stubbornly. "I'll be good for him. Maybe he'll change when we're married. After all, I'm not like his brother's wife, and besides—I'm over thirty!"

In spite of her friend's protests and her own intelligence, Mary let all her rationalizations cloud the issue. She married Jim and it ended in a predictable disaster. They're separated now, but Jim won't agree to a divorce, and Mary is miserable.

"For some reason," her friend said later, "she just couldn't think logically. I don't get it, because Mary's no dope."

THE ONE-TWO-THREE-FOUR-FIVE OF REASON

Like any tool, reason must be used efficiently. All five aspects must be made to work together to cope properly with any situation. Using only discrimination or only objectivity, or even the two, is as if you ran a six-cylinder car on one or two cylinders. It may go, but not as efficiently as it should, and sure as hell it will burn up too much gas. Get all six cylinders working efficiently, and it outperforms any four-cylinder car on the road.

Approach any problem with all five sides of reason used in sequence:

1) *Ambiguity:* See all the possibilities of the problem. Examine all the ramifications. Understand all the ways it might be solved.

2) *Objectivity:* Step back and divorce yourself from the situation. See yourself as someone else would see you. Realize your potential, or lack of it. Is the solution worth finding?

3) *Discrimination:* This is the time to add up the pros and cons. What's good about each possible solution? What's bad?

4) *Detachment:* Ignore the smoke screens of sex, hate, revenge, poverty, wealth, power, and decide what is best for you and those you love.

5) *Logic:* Evaluate the situation and decide what to do—without rationalizing.

[CHAPTER SIX]

Playing the Games of Empathy

REVERSING ROLES

The Kornbergs are a very happy couple. You feel comfortable when you're with them—relaxed. "Maybe because they're so relaxed with each other," a friend suggested. "They never have trouble managing their lives."

They weren't always like that. In fact, five years ago their marriage was almost on the rocks. "We were constantly at each other," Shirley Kornberg said. "Everything I did seemed to annoy Jack, and I never felt he had any sympathy for my problems. Then we had that terrible winter where Jack was laid off, and there just wasn't any work available. Jack's unemployment insurance ran out and we were seriously thinking of welfare when I got my job at the electronics plant.

"After that we had to turn everything upside down. Jack stayed home and took care of the house and baby, and I went to work. Thank God it only lasted a year! Jack found a decent job in Ohio and we pulled up and relocated. I was never cut out to be a breadwinner, but that year shook us up in so many ways."

"What it did," Jack explained seriously "was make each of us understand the other's work. I never realized housework was so bothersome and dull. I didn't know what went into taking care of a kid. Up till then I thought Shirley had it made, staying home every day and doing what she pleased—I resented that."

"And I got a taste of a nine-to-five job," Shirley added. "Now I think both of us understand each other's problems. I know what Jack goes through on the job and he knows what a housewife does."

What Jack and Shirley found in that year of role reversal was empathy for each other. When it comes to getting along with other people, in or out of marriage, empathy is one of the most subtle and valuable of all the coping tools. Very simply, having empathy is having enough sensitivity to know what someone else is feeling, and to experience some of that feeling yourself. It is an understanding so deep that it operates on a gut level. When you empathize with someone it's as if, for the moment, you step into that person's skin.

Jack and Shirley were forced to do it by economics. When they went back to their original jobs, the work they each preferred, they took with them an appreciation of what the other did, an empathy that affected their relationship from then on.

"Once our lives straightened out, we got our heads on straight, too," Shirley explained. "Now Jack can sympathize with all the frustrations I face every day with the house and baby, and I understand the stress he faces at work. It makes it so much easier to cope with each other."

THE IF-I-WERE-YOU GAME

Is empathy something we either have or haven't, or can we learn it? If we have some of it, is there any way to increase it?

Even though some of us are born with a natural flair for empathy, the rest of us can learn it. We can develop any latent empathy we have and discover how to use it as a coping tool. The *Method* school of acting is based on the learning and development of empathy.

To play a part, the actor is taught more than the lines and how to deliver them. He's taught to understand the motivation of the character he portrays. Is the character logical in what he does? What makes him say the things he says? do the things he does? The actor *becomes* the character for the duration of the play, often to the point where he has difficulty getting out of the part afterwards.

It's a more difficult approach to acting than the traditional one, and if it's done properly, it can be very moving. The audience recognizes the actor's empathy with the character in the play, and empathizes with the actor.

If you can learn to empathize with a character in a play, then it's logical to assume that you can learn to empathize with a real character, a husband, wife, friend, parent, child, and sometimes even a stranger. We can't all put as much time into learning empathy as an actor does into learning his craft, but there are tricks we can use to shortcut the process and strengthen our empathy.

ROLE REVERSAL

This is one of the best tricks. The Kornbergs were forced to do it, but they came out of the experience with a strong sense of empathy for each other. But role reversal can be used very deliberately over a short period of time to gain coping empathy. Here are some examples of typical problems where games of role reversal helped some troubled people to cope.

The Overwhelming Father

Herb loves his kids, but he can't teach them anything without taking over and doing it himself. "It's easier that way," he says defensively, but the kids say, "It makes us feel stupid and useless." As a result, they do less around the house, and Herb can't understand why or how to cope with them.

Herb agreed to some role-reversal games in order to straighten things out within the family. The first was with his son, a bicycle freak, who agreed to show Herb how to put the chain on his ten-speed gear assembly. His son, however, never allowed Herb to finish.

"Here, let me do it. It's easier," he assured Herb as he took over. The same routine was used by ten-year-old Janie who showed her father how to hook a rug, doing it all herself, and by Herb's wife, who taught him how to bake a cake without even letting him crack an egg.

"I got the point," Herb admitted. "But only after I was frustrated myself. Now I think I know how the kids feel. This week my boy helps me fix the car, and I promise him—hands off!"

The Arrogant Boss

After five years of flawless work, secretary Hazel Banja tells her boss she's quitting. Dismayed, he says, "You can't. You're the best girl I've ever had. This place would go to pot without you. If it's more money . . ."

Hazel says, "No. Money doesn't enter into it. It's your attitude."

"My attitude?" Bewildered, he shakes his head. "What have I done?"

"Like calling me the best girl."

"But you are!"

"Damn it," Hazel says furiously. "I'm not. I'm almost forty. I'm no girl. You just don't see me. I'm not a person to you. I'm a stick of furniture till you want something, and then you treat me as if I were fifteen years old!"

Simply because he knew he couldn't get along without her, Hazel's boss suggested they try a game of role reversal for a couple of days. "Not work," he explained. "I couldn't begin to do yours—though maybe you could do mine. But let's try reversing the way we treat each other."

Dubious at first, Hazel caught on quickly. She called him by his first name, praised him to her associates—"That boy is a good worker"—ordered him about as casually as he had ordered her, and accepted the coffee-break drinks he brought her without bothering to thank him.

In turn, he called her Mrs. Banja, asked her if she'd please do this or that, and in general treated her as a secretary treats a boss.

"It opened both our eyes," Hazel admitted. "I'm staying on now, and I can see that a lot of the problem was mine, too. I didn't really understand my boss's outlook."

"I think the little game helped me become sensitive to Hazel as a human being," her boss explained. "It wasn't easy for me because I was giving up my dominant role, but it made me realize how arrogant I had been."

The Lazy Lover

Ethel and Bert have a simple sexual problem. When Bert is satisfied, sexually, he is no longer interested in lovemaking. "Enough is enough. I just want to turn over and go to sleep."

"And I still feel keyed up," Ethel says unhappily. "I don't want to come down like a deflated balloon. I want to drift down like a parachute."

"So drift, but let me go to sleep."

When it looked as if this single problem was going to break up their relationship, both agreed to try a reversal game. "But how can we do it?" Bert spread his hands. "How can I put myself in Ethel's place? I feel what I feel."

Ethel smiled. "Let me try."

The next time they made love, just before Bert reached his peak, Ethel drew back and turned away. "Bert, I'm tired. I want to go to sleep."

"Well, sure, but let's finish first."

"I am finished, Bert. That's just it."

Angrily, Bert said, "Speaking of a deflated balloon . . ."

Ethel smiled lazily. "Why don't you drift down like a parachute while I go to sleep?"

"I had a dozen quick reactions," Bert admitted later. "But my strongest one was I just wanted to belt her one. Later, thinking it over, I realized that I'd never coped with the problem before because I never understood how Ethel felt. That little game put me right in her shoes, and man—for the first time it hit me!"

THE BARRIERS TO EMPATHY

Many people don't need role reversal to feel empathy. To them, feeling empathy is doing what comes naturally and it not only helps them cope with their family, friends, and lovers, but also with their jobs. The salesman with a heavy dose of empathy understands his clients. He senses when the moment is right for a hard sell because he feels so much of what the client feels. In the same way he knows when to hold back, or to try a soft sell. Often he knows it without knowing that he does—he's a natural.

The labor mediator who is most successful is the one who feels empathy for both sides. He can put himself in the worker's shoes or the boss's because he senses how both feel. He appreciates their gripes and knows their weaknesses and strengths.

The father in empathy with his son can overcome the generation gap. He realizes how important it is for the boy to look like the other kids, to wear the same hairstyles and clothes. He knows how much his son has to resist him and do things on his own, because he too can feel the way his son feels.

The same is true for mothers and daughters, but as a rule women tend to have more empathy than men. Perhaps it's part of the nesting instinct, the mothering act, or perhaps the culture puts more emphasis on a woman being sensitive and receptive. Sensitivity is a term we use to define femininity. By contrast, men are taught to be *cool,* to stand on their own two feet and not be too sympathetic. Toughness is manliness.

For the teacher who must handle children, empathy is a prime coping tool. There is a natural barrier between pupil and teacher, and the teacher must cope with the barrier before she can teach.

The motion picture *Conrack* showed a situation where the barrier was even stronger because of the racial problem. The teacher was white, the students black. Empathy tore the barrier down. It can also tear down other barriers.

Florence, who taught third grade in a public school in a poor neighborhood found that her own affluence was a barrier between her and her students. "When I first came here," she said, "it was like a nightmare. I wasn't used to kids like these. I came from a sheltered, middle-class family, and these kids weren't used to me. They didn't trust me, and every day I'd be talking to a sea of cold, closed faces and eyes that said, 'Prove yourself!'

"I thought I'd never make it, and my only hope was to get through the first year and transfer—or else quit. Then, in one afternoon, it all changed. The principal suspected one of the boys, Tommy, of marking the blackboards with graffiti, but he couldn't prove it. I came into class one day and caught Tommy redhanded, spraying my board. I took the can away and we were both standing in front of the class while I searched for something devastating to say—I really felt hateful—when the door opened and the principal walked in.

"He took in the situation and said, 'I see we have a little problem!' He was mentally licking his lips, and at that moment, and I don't know why, everything shifted focus for me. Suddenly I knew what Tommy felt—the defiance, not maliciousness, that had gone into his graffiti.

"I acted instinctively. I put my arm around Tommy's shoulders and smiled at the principal. 'Tommy's going to help me clean the board. I sprayed it for the class to see how hard it is to get paint off. It's a good object lesson, don't you think?'

"There was nothing he could do. He bawled me out later for encouraging vandalism with my demonstration—I guess he suspected the truth, but the amazing thing was what happened to me, to Tommy, and to the rest of the class. The barrier was down. We all understood each other and I was on their side against unreasoning authority. The rest of that term was a dream. Tommy was my protector, and I was able to teach him and the rest of the class. Oh, there are still problems, and I guess there always will be, but the big thing is—I can cope!"

THE OBJECTIVE WITNESS

The barrier this teacher faced was economic. It could also have been cultural, racial, religious, or the barrier between the sexes. Basically, the problem narrows down to a lack of understanding. Neither side knows what the other feels, and so they project their own suspicions and fears across the barrier.

What sometimes helps is an impartial third party to point out objective reality. An empathy game based on this solution helped Sally and Adam. They hadn't been married long, but they both felt they were about to split up.

"We can't talk things over," Sally complained. "Adam just doesn't listen. I say one thing and he hears something else."

"The truth is," Adam protested, "you say something, and a minute later you contradict what you said."

The marriage counselor who was trying to help them suggested a little game where an impartial third party sat in on their arguments. "How can we do that?" Adam asked. "When we argue in front of you it's one thing, but when we argue at home . . ."

"I have an idea about that," the counselor said. "What both of you want is an objective report of your arguments. Why not try a tape recorder. If you can put it on and forget about it, when you play it back it should solve all your arguments about who said what."

Sally and Adam agreed, but oddly enough there wasn't any need to play back the recorder. "What happened," Sally explained, "was that we were both so aware of the recorder that we began listening to each other just so we wouldn't be embarrassed later—and that was a breakthrough."

"I think we both realized," Adam said, "that what we both needed and wanted was to understand each other, to get behind the words to what we each felt—but first we had to hear the words."

The tape recorder, by forcing them to listen to each other, strengthened their empathy so that they could cope with the threatened breakup of their marriage.

MAKE A LITTLE LIST

Any relationship is strengthened if there is empathy and weakened if empathy is missing. But how can you tell if you really have empathy for someone before becoming involved, or even after?

One good method is making a list. It's an offshoot of role reversal, and it's most effective when a problem arises. Sy and Ritchie used it when they ran into a problem in their small business. They were equal partners, but Sy ran the shop and Ritchie the office. The problems in each place were different, just as the work was different, and from the very beginning neither could understand the other's problems.

"The trouble is," Ritchie told Sy, "you don't understand that I can't always order the best equipment. I can't always give credit to a guy when you promise it."

"Maybe so, but you don't realize it's no picnic running a shop. You promise things I can't deliver. You make time schedules that don't work out."

To keep the business going, Sy and Ritchie had to work together, not at cross purposes. But no matter how much they talked they couldn't see each other's viewpoint. Then, at a friend's suggestion, each sat down and tried to make a list of all the complaints *the other had.* Sy tried his best to list Ritchie's grievances as Ritchie felt them while Ritchie tried to list Sy's complaints.

"It made me think," Ritchie said. "All of a sudden I was finding fault with myself."

"Me, too," Sy laughed. "I dug up more reasons than Ritchie could why I was bollixing things up."

It was a beginning, a first step toward empathy, and with Sy and Ritchie it worked. They were able to understand a little more about each other, enough to break through their problems.

List making works best when the people concerned face some barrier that blocks empathy. A teacher I know used a variation of this in a class of integrated children. By midterm the black and white children knew each other, but were suspicious and mistrustful.

The teacher had each white child pretend he was black and each black child pretend he was white. Then they were asked to write essays about the best thing that had happened to them in the past month—and the worst thing.

"It didn't do away with all the tension," she told me. "Some of the children just couldn't make the transition. But many could, and they found that suddenly they were looking at the world through different eyes. It not only affected their viewpoints, but it also affected the way they treated their classmates."

List making can often bring empathy to a marriage turning bad. It holds up a mirror in which you can see the reflection of your own problems as your wife or husband sees them. Through empathy it can bring objectivity.

TOO MUCH OF A GOOD THING

While empathy can be a great help in coping with other people, too much of it can also be a hazard. I knew a brilliant young neurosurgeon who after ten years of remarkable work in brain surgery threw it all over to change his field completely and start out again in hand surgery.

When I asked why he gave up such a promising career, he shrugged. "Promising? Sure. I was good and I knew it, but I was being destroyed by the work."

"Why?"

"Because I identified with every patient. I became involved with each one. I was too sympathetic, too concerned about their lives. I got to know them, to understand them, and to feel with them—and for most of them there was no answer to their illness. I'd operate, knowing how slim the chances were, but there was no other choice. So few survived—so damned few, and then, as often as not, the brain was too damaged to do them any good."

He shook his head. "I just couldn't stand it, no matter how exciting the challenge and the work. I got out of it. Look, you don't lose a patient with hand surgery, and if you're good, your success rate is tremendous!"

In his case, too much empathy, too much sensitivity, had made him unable to cope with his work. He couldn't cut back on his empathy. So he changed his work.

USING EMPATHY CREATIVELY

Empathy is one of the subtlest, but most creative of all the coping tools. It is, basically, the ability to understand someone else, to put yourself in his shoes, to know what makes him tick. When you have this, you also have a complete understanding of the puzzling why of human behavior.

Almost everyone has some degree of empathy. In some people it's well-developed; in others it's dormant. But however little we have, the amount can be increased with games borrowed from method acting and psychiatry. Role reversal, calling an impartial witness, making lists—all these are games designed to increase an awareness of others, and as we become aware of others we cannot help but empathize with them.

[CHAPTER SEVEN]

Using Pretense, Dreams, and Fantasy as Coping Tools

WHAT WENT ON IN HISTORY

If we could hook a tape recorder to a time machine and send it back to listen to famous people at critical moments in their lives, what they really said would probably have no resemblance to what historians and biographers tell us they said.

In his last years of exile, brooding on the relentless waves that pounded Elba's shores, did Napoleon liken them to the alliance that had defeated him at Waterloo? Probably not. The odds are all that he was daydreaming, "What if ten ships and a hand-picked army are right now waiting in the fog off shore. Let's say one of their boats slips in with muffled oars and news from Talleyrand that that Bourbon weakling can't hack it, and they have to have me back . . ."

Or Cleopatra, drifting down the Nile with Antony in those final days—was she considering man's brief mortality and the nobility of suicide in preference to defeat, or was she thinking, "What if Octavian doesn't mean us any harm and they're only coming after us to tell us that Antony is forgiven and they need us both in Rome to straighten out the city . . ."

Or Washington at Valley Forge, huddled over the meager warmth of a campfire. Was he giving humble thanks to God that there was still a handful of ragged men left, or was he dreaming, "There are a hundred wagons with supplies and men camped just beyond the Schuylkill River, and as soon as this mucking snow lets up they'll roll into camp with food and clothes and boots and ammunition . . ."

Or Socrates, considering the hemlock. Did he really come up with those moving last words, or did he think, "What if it's not really poison. Maybe it's just to test my integrity, and once I've taken it they'll explain how right I was and we'll all go off to the baths . . ."

Historians would like us to believe that great men and women never needed daydreams to bolster them up. They coped with life by facing it squarely. But historians were never a reliable source of reality. It's far more likely that the beautiful people of history needed their little fantasies to cope just as much as we need ours today.

THE WHEN-MY-SHIP-COMES-IN GAME

During the depression years of the thirties, I had a friend whose family, like mine, was scraping the bottom of the economic barrel. Irv's father had been in the garment industry, but when that went bad he became a butcher's assistant. Irv and his brothers, with the rest of us, delivered for the local storekeepers for a nickel an order.

Their entire family income was under twenty-five dollars a week, but I enjoyed hanging out at Irv's home in the evenings much more than at my own. At my house there was an air of dejection. We were always aware of the threat of bad times, the ever-present fear that tomorrow a job would be lost, we wouldn't meet the rent, the bills would mount up.

It wasn't like that at Irv's. They *knew* things would get better. Irv's father was ready for a "break" and then he'd start in business for himself. Irv's mother entered contests, and one of these days her "ship would come in."

I'd sit at the dining room table with them, delighting in their dreams and plans; how they'd spend the money, where they'd go, what schools the boys would attend. I'd close my eyes and see the shock on the boss's face when Irv's father dropped into the store in a "Homburg and a gray gabardine, a black wool coat with a caracul collar, and maybe a cane, a very slim Malacca."

"Oh, yes, you've got to have a cane!"

I would gasp with delight when his mother told how she'd furnish the apartment, hire a maid, buy a velvet coat with a mink collar for evening wear.

"Sable, Mom!" one of the boys would say ecstatically.

She'd consider for a moment. "Sable's too much. We don't want to flaunt it, just let them all know that we've got it."

Irv's father and mother died penniless. When I met him many years later, a prosperous accountant, he told me, "Nothing could have lived up to the plans we made, the constant expectations, those crazy daydreams—but what the hell, they got us through."

He was right. The daydreams of his parents were the strongest tool they had to cope with all those years of marginal living. Fantasy helps sustain most of us in times of despair or poverty. Sometimes we build our fantasy around contests we'll win the way Irv's mother did. Sometimes it's a lottery ticket, that one big sale, that crazy business deal, that really beautiful stock—a sleeper!

Usually we have the fantasy under control. Deep down, we know that it is fantasy, but we use it to give ourselves an extra charge, a little more strength to cope with the world.

THE DREAMS WE NEED

In Steinbeck's *Of Mice and Men,* George used fantasy to cope with simple-minded Lennie, and he taught

Lennie to use it as a coping device against a hostile world. In the end, when Lennie went beyond the point where fantasy would let him deal with reality, George put a gun to his head and killed him in the middle of his fantasy.

Playwrights have always recognized the importance of fantasy in coping with life, and often they are intrigued with what happens to a person when his fantasies are destroyed. Does he become weaker or stronger? Edward Albee, in *Who's Afraid of Virginia Woolf?,* had the wife use an imaginary child to cope with her own empty life. When the husband deliberately sets out to destroy her fantasy, all hell breaks loose, but the couple emerge stronger than before.

In *Play It Again, Sam,* Woody Allen uses an imaginary Humphrey Bogart to teach his hero to cope with women. In Schaffer's *Equus,* when the protagonist's fantasies are destroyed, the psychiatrist wonders if he's done a good or an evil thing by destroying them, likening the process to man's loss of God.

In O'Neill's *Long Day's Journey into Night,* the mother can function as long as she can keep her fantasies. She can ignore her own drug addiction and the alienation of her family. But when her fantasy is taken away, she is destroyed.

Again and again the same theme is sounded. People need fantasies to cope with a world that is too frightening, too senseless, or too cold and heartless. The fantasies give them something the real world lacks, and this is the basic rule behind the use of fantasy as a coping device.

After World War II, a study in the *American Journal of Psychiatry* explored some of the psychological techniques used by prisoners attempting to survive in a Nazi concentration camp. The prisoners were not only threatened with physical death, but also with mental disintegration. To destroy them, the Nazi captors "broke down the barriers of culture," hoping to take away any semblance of humanity.

According to the author, the prisoners searched for support from each other by forming political groups. In the process of survival, religious faith died away. But very often, "in search of some form of satisfaction, the prisoners turned to fantasy." This became a positive coping tool in their attempt to stay human.

In fantasy, the coper can find the strength he needs to use his own coping skills, or he can examine the fears that prevent him from using those skills, or in some cases he can use fantasy as a defense against the truth. The truth may be too harsh to face, too destructive. A fantasy can either soften the truth about yourself—"I'm as good as he is"—or overcome the opposition—"He thinks he's great stuff, but he's really a phony."

THE FANTASY PUT-DOWN

I remember a couple at a vacation resort who used fantasy to destroy others and cope with their own inadequacy. They were in their mid-fifties, a sour, defeated pair who didn't have a kind word for anyone. They'd sit at a table in the corner during meals and dissect everyone in audible whispers.

"There goes little Miss Hot-pants with another. Is this her sixth or seventh for the week? For someone with nothing at all . . ."

"This is their chicken Kiev? I could do better with an old rooster!"

"That tennis pro! If it wasn't for this leg I could play rings around him."

"Get that dress. If she had half your taste . . ."

And they would go on and on, attacking everything and everybody with a stream of critical fantasy, as if by making others seem bad they could convince themselves that they were good, indeed the best.

They were the most obvious players in this put-down game, but there are other players whose fantasy is not as venomous and it's hard to decide whether their method of coping is completely negative. There is a couple I know, happily married, genuinely in love with each other, but unable, no matter how hard they try, to make ends meet.

The problem is Bob, the husband, a decent, pleasant man who just isn't very competent or talented in his profession. He rarely holds a job for more than a year at a time.

Many men would be crushed by this and would consider themselves failures. Not Bob. For one thing, his wife wouldn't allow that to happen. She copes with his failure by sending up a smoke screen of fantasy. Within the shelter of the screen Bob functions happily without ever seeing his own weakness.

If he runs into trouble on the job, she quickly finds a whipping boy. "Your boss is jealous. He knows he hasn't got your talent. How can they expect you to do the work without the right kind of help? At the salary they pay, they're lucky to get someone as good as you. They're out to get you . . ." and so on, all calculated to hide Bob's basic weakness.

She puts up the smoke screen skillfully, selling the fantasy to herself as well as Bob so that they can both accept it. If this ploy is going to work, it's because neither sees how weak Bob is.

This is a very common coping defense, and to one extent or another we all use it. We justify our weaknesses and failures with small pretenses that somehow or other exonerate us. We also fire up the smoke screen for those we love.

Sometimes the fantasy gets out of hand and we are

truly convinced that we are better than we are, and we take on jobs that we cannot possibly accomplish. Or we convince our friends, our lovers, our children that they are really doing well when common sense should tell us that they aren't.

The distinction here is between using a fantasy to cope with the world, or using it to escape from the world. It isn't an easy distinction because we often cope with the world by escaping for short periods. Literature offers such an escape, and so does television, while movies have always been classic escape machines.

We use all of them for moments of escape, but to try to escape *into* them never works. In one of the classic fantasies of childhood, *Alice in Wonderland,* Alice escapes into a dream world, but spends the entire book anxiously trying to return to reality. In the *Wizard of Oz* Dorothy, too, moves from adventure to adventure in an attempt to get home to Kansas. The authors, creating their worlds of escape, still recognize the perspective of fantasy and assure their child readers that no matter how much fun fantasy is, reality is what we need and want.

You can't escape reality and still remain sane. The recluse or hermit is an example. He will often fill his retreat with all the memorabilia of his fantasy world—a time long gone. Sometimes his escape route consists of wearing the old-fashioned clothes of that past, happy time, and though he mingles with the rest of the world, he's locked into his own private fantasy.

All of us are guilty of this same process, but to a smaller degree. We all look back on "the good old days" when things were simpler and the world was smaller, the sunshine brighter and the summer longer.

Today's craze for nostalgia is a symptom of this fantasy, and it seems to get stronger as the world threatens to come apart at the seams. We turn to artifacts of the thirties and forties, Art Deco of the twenties and Art Nouveau of the turn of the century, to any time but the here and now. We turn to the past to escape, but our turning strengthens us to cope with today. It convinces us that there were once endless summers and simpler times and they may come again.

The sad irony is that the good old days are only a fantasy. The present was always bad because that was what you had to cope with.

STRENGTH THROUGH FANTASY

Does that mean that we shouldn't look back? That it's wrong to hold onto our dreams of yesterday? Not at all. This is simply another way to use fantasy to cope. When the fantasy is used purposefully and properly, when we keep control of it, it becomes a valid tool.

This is true at any age. Children start their coping with a rich use of fantasy. They handle frustration with it. Take five-year-old Sherry. Her father told her she couldn't play with his power tools. She wanted to be like Daddy and use them, but she also knew she had to obey. To overcome her frustration she built up a common childhood fantasy.

"The big saw doesn't like little girls. When Daddy is here he won't let the saw hurt me, but if I go near the saw alone it'll get me! I hate him and I won't play with him. I won't play with anyone I hate."

As a little girl, Sherry used fantasy to water away the tension of her frustration. As she grew older her ability to fantasize increased. Her loneliness grew less when she peopled it with imaginary friends. Finally she invented a steady, imaginary girl friend, stronger, wiser, and more daring than she was. She called her Sharon, and Sharon became more than a playmate to cope with loneliness. She was also a convenient scapegoat. "I didn't do it. Sharon did." Or, "Sharon made me do it."

Sometimes Sharon tested things out for her. "She ran

across the street and wasn't hit. She lit a match and didn't get burned."

Sherry's fears were also assuaged with fantasy in the form of magic. "No one can hurt me when I wear my magic bracelet. If I walk down the sidewalk and don't step on cracks I won't break my mother's heart. If I wish on the first star I'll be healthy and happy all my life."

This childhood magic is similar to the magic used by primitive men. When they wanted animals in their hunting grounds, they drew pictures of the animals on cave walls or modeled them in clay. By sympathetic magic the animals were drawn to the area.

They used fantasy to cope, but with a difference. Primitive men believed in their magic. From our vantage point in time we can consider it fantasy, but they didn't. They knew it worked. To them it was reality.

The same is true of children. They use fantasy differently because they believe in their magic. As they grow up the belief dies, but the magic lingers. Adults still throw salt over their shoulders and still knock on wood.

When Sherry was very young and first started to walk, her parents ignored her failures and said, "Look at her go. Isn't that wonderful? She's walking!" The little fantasy encouraged Sherry and she kept on trying.

When she was much older, six years old, she learned to make potholders, and her mother couldn't wait to show her father Sherry's first miserable attempts. "Aren't these splendid potholders? They're just what I needed. They'll look beautiful in the kitchen."

Sherry, encouraged and exhilarated by the praise, went on to more careful work and finally turned out excellent potholders. Looking back on her earlier attempts, she wondered what her parents saw in them, but put their enthusiasm down to the blindness of love.

But it wasn't blind love. It was her parents' conscious fantasy to encourage her developing skills. All parents feed children small fantasies to help them cope with difficult tasks. Later in life the encouragement job is taken over by teachers, friends, lovers, and eventually by their children.

I knew a man who began to paint in his sixties, after retirement. His first attempts were ordinary, but his children were so delighted that he had finally taken up a hobby that they built up all sorts of fantasies about his paintings, begging for new ones to hang in their homes.

Pleased, he continued and finally became good enough to look back realistically at his earlier work. "It was awful," he told me. "But without the kids' praise I'd never have kept at it."

THE FANTASY THAT DESTROYS

Using fantasy like this is not an easy thing, and often it can have uncomfortable results. The fantasy can make demands beyond the ability of the person you want to help. The mother who would make her klutzy daughter into a dancer, or the father who sees his uncoordinated son as an athlete are not helping their children. They're simply using the children to act out their own fantasies.

When the goal is too much, the fantasy builds up frustration. Johnny's parents smothered him with this kind of fantasy. If he drew a picture he had incredible talent. If he wrote a composition he was a future Hemingway. Let him pick out a tune on the piano and he was another Henry Mancini. They wanted a son they could boast about, but Johnny saw all their praise as impossible expectations.

In a kind of despair, Johnny switched from one college major to another and finally dropped out in his twenties. "I want a job with no demands," he said. "I don't want any advancement or raises—just something to bring in a buck."

The same destructive use of fantasy occurs when a wife sets up impossible goals for her husband. "You'll be part of management in a year, John. Wait and see." Or when the husband sets up equally unrealistic goals for his wife. "Mary is a fantastic housekeeper. She does wonders with those kids."

The point is, there must be rules for the fantasy if it is to work as a coping device. The success you daydream, for yourself or others, must be possible and believable. There has to be a gentle balance between fantasy and reality. The moment fantasy leaves reality too far behind, it becomes an anti-coping device leading to frustration and self-destruction.

THE PARADOX OF TESTING

One of the ways we use fantasy is in testing. We dream up the worst thing that can happen to us and try it on for size. Often we do it consciously with daydreams or by reading books about someone else's terrible experience or by seeing disaster movies of earthquakes, capsized ocean liners, and burning skyscrapers. In this type of movie we live through the very worst—and still walk out of the theater.

Sometimes we "test" unconsciously with our dreams. Our nightmares of death and separation from those we love are dream-world trials of what we dread facing but know we must.

I knew a woman who told me of a terrible dream she had a few weeks before. Her husband and children were killed in it and she had awakened crying bitterly. What bothered her all the next day was not the dream, but the fact that she felt a profound feeling of relief.

"It was almost as if I had been through the worst and nothing more could happen," she told me uncomfortably. "I feel a little guilty that I'm not worried about the dream coming true."

But the dream had discharged her worry. She had tested the very worst that could happen and had survived. Though consciously she was uneasy, unconsciously she felt relief.

There are times when we don't seem to be content with daydreams and nightmares as coping tools. We take a step beyond and try to turn the dreadful fantasy into reality. We pick a fight with someone we love in order to test his love. Will he feel the same afterwards? We deliberately get into dangerous situations to see if they are as bad as we feared. We may drive recklessly, swim where the current is too strong, walk dangerous streets—take all sorts of chances in order to act out our fantasies and test our fears.

Ultimately, there are some people who test their greatest fear—death. Paradoxically, they commit suicide because they are so afraid to die. Their method of coping has gotten completely out of control.

This is using fantasy as a coping device beyond the point of no return, to the point where it becomes deadly. We must learn where that point lies. We must *use* fantasy instead of letting it use us.

SEX AND FANTASY

Sex without fantasy is good by itself, but fantasy makes it even better. In some cases it does more. It lets us respond sexually to someone who just doesn't turn us on.

Take the case of Arlene. She was married to a much older man, and while she felt no sexual excitement with him, she did love him very deeply. "Arnold isn't just a breadwinner," she told her sister defensively. "I wouldn't want any kind of life without him. He's warm and kind and good. The trouble is . . ."

"The trouble is," her sister finished, "he's no Rex Harrison even if he is the same age. He's more like a poor man's Robert Morley. I'm sorry, Sis. I didn't mean to hurt your feelings. He's a great guy, but I can't imagine you getting—well, excited about him."

"I don't," Arlene sighed. "I'll level with you. I close my eyes and think of Steve McQueen, and I think hard! But honestly, I'd rather die than ever let Arnold know. It's not wrong if it helps me—love him? Is it?"

"I don't think it's wrong," her sister said firmly. "If it helps."

It did help, and Arlene isn't alone in using this kind of mental gymnastics. Thousands of men and women do. We all learn to fantasize as children when we learn to masturbate, and we continue the fantasy as adults until it becomes so linked to sexual response that eventually we respond to the fantasy alone. For young men the fantasy is usually women—for young women, men.

Arlene, with many other men and women, fantasizes during sex because her partner doesn't live up to her earlier fantasies. If he becomes adept enough at this psycho-hanky-panky, any husband can take Raquel Welch or Ann-Margret to bed each night of his marriage, and any wife can take Burt Reynolds or Warren Beatty.

In fact no one has to stop at Hollywood sex symbols. Every man or woman in the street, in books, on television is available. Sex makes no difference. You can mix and match without protest. Fantasy has few bounds.

Is all of this good or bad? It really doesn't matter. If sexual fantasy helps you cope without hurting someone else or yourself, then it's a valid coping tool.

Inevitably, the use of fantasy in sex has been exploited in our society. Today's pornographic market packages and sells sexual fantasies in and out of plain brown wrappers, in motion pictures, in sex shops, and in magazines. Pornography has been given a bad press, but the only real danger from it—according to a number of reliable studies—is that too much defeats itself. It dampens the sexual appetite.

A little of it, however, can do a world of good. Drs. John Money and Robert Athanasiou suggested, in the *American Journal of Obstetrics and Gynecology,* that when a woman watches pornography on the screen, she fancies herself as the actress and the man she loves as the actor. A man, on the other hand, while he sees himself as the actor, "takes the actress down from the screen in fantasy," and has at her then and there!

And afterwards? Scientists who have studied the matter note that both men and women pretend indifference, but secretly get a much greater charge out of sex after seeing the screen lovers. The fantasy they saw is still vivid enough to turn them on a little more.

THE SHAPE OF THINGS TO COME

What it all adds up to is that fantasy, pretense, and dreams are all ways in which we can rehearse our coping procedures. In our make-believe worlds we can test out every possible method of coping with life. Since they are all fantasy tests we can be as creative as we like, and later, when we put some of these methods to the test, we'll be doing something we may not have done before, but certainly something we've rehearsed. It has to be better this time around.

[CHAPTER EIGHT]

Masking and Control: Are They Valid Coping Tools?

THE JANUS FACTOR

Ellis's job is to supervise the work of a dozen men. "One thing about Ellis," one of the men under him said, "he's consistent—a bastard every time."

The men above Ellis couldn't believe the occasional reports they heard about him. "This is a very sweet guy," his immediate superior said. "He's always ready to do a favor, always helpful and pleasant. Gets his job done quickly. There must be a couple of bad apples in that crew of his."

Was Ellis two different people, a schizoid personality? Not at all. He was simply a perfect example of the Janus Factor in action. In essence, the Janus Factor says that every man within a corporation has two faces. One face is turned toward the people higher up in the corporate structure; the other toward those lower down.

A corollary of the Janus Factor is that the more secure the person is in the corporate structure, the less difference there is between his two faces. The president of Ellis's company has only one face on view. Of course it is always turned downward toward everyone under him, and no one at work ever sees the face he presents to his wife and children.

Oh yes, there is one other person in the company with just one face, the lowest man on the corporate totem pole. That's Alex in maintenance. He faces upward only. There's no one below him, and he's rather genial and pleasant to everyone—everyone is his superior. He lives by himself and we have no record of the face he presents to his dog and cat.

The Janus Factor is best observed in industry, but it also applies to politics. In the recent Watergate affair that ended with Richard Nixon's resignation, the nation saw one face of Nixon, a calm, rational man in control. The secret tapes disclosed a completely different face of Nixon, vulgar and out of control. Were the two faces one man? Certainly. It was the Janus Factor in action.

The factor applies on every level. Take Sally, a sunny housewife and mother. She is spun sugar to her husband, loving and docile. She's ready to help any neighbor, in fact Sally is a one-woman welcome wagon. When someone moves in she's there at once with a cold meal and a warm hello. When there's trouble in any home, you can count on Sally, always to help, never to interfere.

But to her own children Sally presents quite a different face. She's a tough disciplinarian and frequently flies off the handle.

Sally was married for ten years and things might have gone on for another ten, but suddenly, unexpectedly, Sally had a nervous breakdown. It was a rough time for the family, and afterwards Sally started to attend a group session for therapy.

"The only way I can cope with people," she finally admitted to the group, "is by holding back my true feelings. I know I'm a Pollyanna—at least that's the way I try to make people see me. The only ones I let my hair down with are the kids. I guess they're the only ones I'm sure of. I know they'll love me no matter what I am."

"And your husband?" someone asked.

In a low voice Sally said, "If he ever really knew me,

knew what I'm truly like, I think he'd be ashamed of me. He might even leave me!"

Sally's masking is done out of insecurity. There are other members of her therapy group who mask for other reasons. Mike's masking is based on fear. "The only way I can cope is by holding back my true feelings," he tells the group. "I'm the original Mr. Nice Guy—at least that's the way everyone sees me."

"How do you see yourself?" someone asks.

"Inside, I'm a powder keg, ready to blow up." He shivers. "If I ever started telling people how I really felt, I don't know where I'd stop or what I'd say."

Mike is genuinely afraid of his true feelings and of what might happen if he ever let go and acted honestly. But his fear may be without real foundation. "Nice guys" are often making a desperate bid for affection. "Look at me. I'm harmless. You wouldn't hurt a harmless man."

Sally feared rejection. Mike needed love. They both masked to get what they wanted. People mask for other reasons, to get power, security, status. Sally and Mike are extreme cases, yet everyone, to some degree, masks his true feelings in order to cope with life. We all feel we would be too vulnerable if we didn't.

The simplest mask is the noncommittal look, the expressionless face, and yet expression itself is a masking device. A smile is the easiest way of hiding unhappiness, anger, or disappointment. A grim look can mask joy and elation, a frown can cover up happiness.

Some of us use more than expression to mask. Women use makeup to exaggerate their eyes, emphasize their lips, create a blush on their cheeks, a soft down on their skin.

Men use hair to project a different image or to cover up their own. A full moustache can be a mask of virility, a beard can change the contours of the face or strengthen a receding chin, add a touch of wisdom, a bit of cool.

LEARNING TO MASK

When does masking start? As far as we know, it's present in early childhood. Most children approach strange adults with solemn faces and wary eyes, giving nothing of themselves, holding back their true feelings. The bright child learns very early what the adult expects and masks accordingly. He generally discovers that his inner feelings are unacceptable to society. He has the choice of changing those feelings or burying them, masking them. In most cases they can't be changed, so he covers them up and begins to create an inner, secret world of his own emotions and fantasies.

The teen-ager becomes even more adept at masking as his changing body releases a flood of hormones that sharpen his desires and needs. He doesn't dare reveal them, and yet he's not quite as skillful at masking as an adult. As a compromise he may settle on the noncommittal mask of childhood or hide behind a sullen look. His parents and teachers write it off as typical of his age, but behind the sullenness there may be a sensitivity too tender to face the world, too frightened, too vulnerable. There is the danger that this masking can be carried too far and end up in a Sally or a Mike.

If we consider all the situations in which all of us use masking, we realize how universal a coping device it is. Politeness, a civilized pleasure of our culture, is simply an elaboration of masking. We mask constantly to cope in business, at school, at home, with our friends—when it comes right down to it, very few of us will dare to expose our inner selves, our true feelings.

This inner self is the most sacred part of man, and we are not expected to reveal it. Masking, in our civilization, is not a bad coping tool nor a harmful one provided it is kept within reasonable limits. In fact, showing our true feelings is often considered wrong and selfish.

Jane, a schoolteacher, tried to explain this in terms of her relationship to her students. "I can't tell them the truth about their work. When they hand in early compositions they're often terrible, ungrammatical, badly spelled. I comment on a few mistakes, the obvious ones, and encourage them to try again. They think they've done well and they go on to do better."

Jane's technique was a form of masking. Sid, a baseball coach, used the same masking. "I never tell the guys what I really think. If I did I might kill some talented players before they got a chance to develop. I have to build them up, make as if they're doing fine. Or if they louse up a game and I know they couldn't help it, I gotta put on an act, make like I feel a lot worse than I do. That's the game."

Lawyers mask in front of the judge. "Yes, your honor," when they want to say, "You're getting senile, you old bat." And the judge masks to the prisoner. "I'm putting you on probation. I want your word that you'll stay out of trouble," when he knows there's no probability of it. Fathers mask to children and doctors to patients, and just about everyone to everyone else.

TAKE OFF THE MASK

A friend with an outwardly happy marriage once told me, "I'd rather walk naked down Fifth Avenue than let my wife see my true feelings."

Physical unmasking is not too difficult. Many people live comfortably in nudist camps. But unmasking the inner self is sometimes impossible. Our masks are armor against a hostile world, and we couldn't cope without them.

In a big city, where crowding is a way of life, we

build up a strong armor of protective masking. In large beehives of apartment houses you find people who live side by side for years without ever really knowing each other.

In a small town, this kind of privacy would be suspicious. Everyone is used to smiling at people in the street, passing the time of day with a neighbor, and even greeting the occasional stranger with a friendly word. In a city, the same casual freedom is difficult. Stop a New Yorker on the street and try to talk to him and he will usually react with panic. You can't intrude on another's privacy.

But the small-towner, for all his friendliness, will still wear his mask as securely as the New Yorker does. We must not confuse privacy with masking. We can live without one as long as we have the protection of the other.

But what happens when we do away with privacy as well as masking? The recent popularity of sensitivity and encounter groups is based on a conscious attempt to bare the inner self, to reach other people on all levels, physical and psychological, to take off the masks and learn to function without them. But what works in an encounter group doesn't necessarily work in life.

Angela came back from a five-day encounter session at a lodge up in the mountains and at first she was wildly enthusiastic. "It was like a completely new way of seeing and feeling. There was a lot of resistance at first. Some guys were just there for kicks, and some gals were so uptight they couldn't let go. But after the second day we began to get it all together. We shook off our defenses and we got to know each other, really know, deep inside."

But a month later Angela's enthusiasm had withered. "I guess it's an idea before its time."

"What do you mean?"

"I mean you can't let down your defenses unless the rest of the world is willing to do it, too. I went back to work on Monday prepared to be honest and open and bang! I had to start lying to people about orders that didn't go out. I had to pretend I was annoyed with the guy from accounting to get him to let me alone. I had to fake all the production schedules to keep people out of trouble—I run right back to square one! I'm back in the rat race, lying and covering up to get along."

Angela could only cope by taking up her mask again.

CONTROL

Once we learn to mask, we are well on the way to learning control. We cannot cope with civilization unless we are able to suppress our harmful and dangerous impulses. Primitive man couldn't live with his neighbors until he learned to control the impulse to heave a rock at them when they annoyed him, or take their food away when he was hungry, or their mates when he was sexually aroused.

We need these same controls to cope with life today. When they weaken, as they do in some of our big cities, when assault, theft, and rape become everyday occurrences, then we and our cities are in trouble. We are forgetting how to cope.

We learn control at an early age. The baby controls her hunger until the bottle comes, learns to control her bowels and her bladder as she grows up, and then learns to control her desires and suppress those that are anti-social.

The very act of learning control can be pleasant because along with control the growing child learns anticipation with all its joys. The gradual refinement of control, the suppression of drives and desires, is what maturity is all about. We even define immaturity as a lack of control.

The immature child who can't or won't learn control is hard to live with. When he wants something, he wants it at once. When he feels angry, he yells or cries or strikes out. When he's hungry he begs and coaxes for food. If he's old enough to get his own food, he eats erratically with no regard for regular hours.

Gavin was like that as a child, and not much better when he grew up. He was unlucky enough to have a mother who gave in easily and catered to his lack of control. When he left home and moved into his own apartment, it quickly took on the same look as Gavin's room at home, junk and clothes everywhere. But Mother wasn't here to pick up each day, and it grew progressively worse.

For a brief period Gavin shared his apartment and his life with a young woman, but Elizabeth moved out before things became too serious. "I can't live like that," she said regretfully. "God knows, I'm not neat, but to just drop anything anywhere, and then wonder where it is when you want it—And meals! I plan dinner for seven and you get hungry at six and fill up on milk and cookies, then just pick at your food."

Gavin shrugged. "Why not eat when you're hungry? Why wait till seven when I'm hungry at six?"

"Because I take all that trouble to prepare something nice." But Elizabeth made no headway in reaching him and eventually gave up. Gavin was upset, but not enough to change. "That's the way I am. I just don't see why I have to be uptight about things. Why do I have to keep a neat home and eat on time? It's not my life-style."

But Gavin's "life-style" spilled over into his work. He started with a good job with an outfit making documentary movies, but he could no more control his work than he could his life—his work was a part of his life. He misplaced important documents, neglected to finish dull projects, failed to change scripts, and eventually lost his job.

It's difficult, as he found out, to be controlled on one

level while you are uncontrolled on another. Control, to be effective, must be exerted in all areas.

Sometimes there's a deceptive charm about the uncontrolled person. We see him as a primitive, a natural man, but the charm thins out when we have to live and work with him. Harold was like that. Unlike Gavin, his lack of control was psychological. He was a man with a quick temper, always into arguments with cab drivers and waiters while his wife and children died quiet deaths of embarrassment.

Most of the time his children avoided him. "No matter what I say, Dad hits the ceiling," his younger son said disgustedly.

His wife coped by humoring him. "Now you know how Daddy is," she'd tell the children with false cheerfulness. "It doesn't take that much effort to keep things calm. Let's just see if we can avoid any arguments."

If pressed about his temper, she'd usually rationalize it. "Harold's a good person. He does have a short fuse, but no one's perfect."

No one is perfect, but most people are able to use control to cope with life. The ones who don't are the gamblers who can't resist a long shot, the wife who can't pass up that bargain, the husband who bought the car because "even if we don't need it, it looks great," the thief who can't resist an easy set-up, or the fat woman who must have that extra piece of cake.

To one degree or another they're all out of control. They cannot, will not, or have not learned to suppress their desires, impulses, or drives.

THE DARK SIDE OF CONTROL

Most coping devices seem to have their negative reflections, and suppression has its opposite, repression or inhibition. Control, or suppression, assumes a direct, conscious management. A clerk in a department store waits on a rather arrogant customer who insists on going through dozens of items to find one he likes. The clerk is annoyed, but it's an old-fashioned store with rigid rules about the customer always being right. The clerk deliberately suppresses his annoyance.

"I think I'll try that one—no, let me see the one you just put away. I don't know, maybe I shouldn't get this color at all . . ."

Calmly, the clerk replaces each box and brings out new ones till the sale is made. He uses control to cope with an unpleasant situation because his job and his family welfare are at stake.

His friend, in a different, unionized store, stretches her control to the limit. "I never insult the customer, but look, I'm a good worker and my union's strong. I treat them like they treat me. They're nasty; I'm nasty. They're nice; I'm a pussycat."

Both these people used control or suppression, but Alicia coped by using repression. She loved her husband, but a religious, rigid upbringing had made her deeply guilty about sex. Unconsciously she felt that to enjoy sex was to sin. She knew she had to submit to it as part of her marriage agreement, but she also knew she shouldn't enjoy it.

As a result, she was frigid, unable to feel any enjoyment during sex. She inhibited the normal reaction of her body, and though she wasn't aware that she was doing it, her inhibition allowed her to go through the sex act without betraying her upbringing.

Another man who used inhibition unconsciously was Carl. He was basically homosexual, yet unable to admit it on a conscious level. He coped with the problem by repressing his sexual ability. He was impotent with women. He satisfied society's demands that he go to bed with them, but he also satisfied his inner demands against making love to them.

It's usually an extremely severe internal conflict that brings out inhibition as a coping device. Control is also a result of conflict—you want to do something but you know you shouldn't. The conflict is open and manageable. When it becomes too great to manage it usually goes underground and the unconscious takes over and copes by inhibiting whatever is in the way. It's protective, but often the protection is not what we really want.

THE GOOD AND THE BAD OF IT

Masking to cover up our true feelings needn't be a negative act. It can be creative in a coping sense. Children do it, and so do teen-agers to cover up sensitive and vulnerable parts of themselves and to gain time to rally their strengths. But adults, too, sometimes find masking a valuable way of coping with life. The hitch: too often the masks become frozen in place. We lose the joys of unmasking simply because we are afraid of exposure.

Control, like masking, is a coping tool so useful we tend to abuse it. We forget that the most exciting part of both masking and control is doing away with them both. The controlled person who finally "lets it all hang out," or the tightly masked person who lets her real self be seen can both experience an intense pleasure in their new freedom.

[CHAPTER NINE]

How to Cope in the Age of Anxiety

TROUBLE IN PARADISE

Many men have tried to build a better mousetrap, but a group of behavioral scientists recently set out to build a better mouse world. These men from the National Institutes of Mental Health constructed a cage city that could accommodate four thousand mice comfortably with all the food they could eat. They adjusted the temperature to mouse comfort, dropped in four breeding couples, and watched to see what would happen.

Predictably there was a population explosion, and in two years the original four had grown to two thousand. But unpredictably, it was all downhill after that until, four and a half years after it was started, the colony died out.

Curiously, there had always been enough food, water, and living room. There was no serpent in this paradise, and yet something went wrong. The last thousand mice born were fat and beautiful, but passive, withdrawn, and not aggressive. They refused to leave their nests, and also refused to relate to each other, even sexually. They coped with the boredom of a perfect world by turning off.

The Bible tells us that God shooed Adam and Eve

out of Eden as soon as stress reared its ugly head. Once they left Eden, they first started to cope. The mouse Eden, however, worked the other way around. Once the stress was removed, the mice stopped coping.

What was the real Biblical message? Man must cope because he sinned? Or is it that man cannot cope unless he is driven by the stress of reality? Did God do man a favor by kicking him out of Eden?

THE ANXIETY SPECTRUM

Stress is the outside force that causes us to cope. John loses a sale. May's baby won't sleep. Sue's boyfriend takes someone else out. Al's wife is angry at him. The Murphys' baby-sitter doesn't show up. These are all stresses that work on John, Sue, May, and the rest. Under these stresses they feel uneasy. Something is wrong. They're unhappy, sad—in short, they suffer anxiety.

Most of us handle these small anxieties without too much trouble. In fact, we usually react to them by coping. As an example, you have to meet a friend for dinner and suddenly it's later than you think. You feel anxious about getting there on time, so you cope by taking a cab. Or you have to address a meeting and you're anxious about your speech. You cope by studying it very carefully, and as a result you do well at the meeting.

Many of us handle even stronger stresses by coping. Take the case of Jim. He was a senior in high school and like most of his classmates he wanted to get into a good college. Some of the kids in Jim's class found the whole business of applications and interviews too overwhelming. At least three decided to "just drop out and to hell with the whole hassle."

Jim, in spite of his anxiety, never really doubted that he would be accepted, and once in college would make out pretty well. "Sure, I'm just as upset as the other kids," he told his school advisor. "But I know one of the colleges is going to accept me."

"So you're not worried?"

Jim shrugged. "Why should I be? We're all in the same boat. The whole class is on the edge of running scared."

"And that doesn't bother you?"

"Just the opposite. If it's happening to all of us, I figure it's normal, so why get into an uproar? Why should I worry?"

Edith, one of Jim's classmates, took an equally optimistic, but slightly different view. "Sure I'm anxious, and I worry about it, but there's a difference between squirrel caging and good, honest worry. I figure, as long as I worry about something it'll work out—that's if I keep my worry under control. It's the heavy worrying, where your mind goes round and round, that hurts."

What they were both saying was that the amount of anxiety they felt was not enough to hurt them. It just kept them on their toes. Edith worried about clothes and the ratio of boys to girls, so she checked both out. She contacted friends at the school and found out what they wore and what the boy situation was. Her anxiety drove her to do something helpful. Jim's anxiety led him to the conclusion that his situation was normal since everyone else felt the same way.

In both cases anxiety was a positive force that drove the two students to cope with the situation. The stress that caused their anxiety was mild. For other students in their class, the same stress seemed greater, and to a few it seemed too much to handle.

One man's stress is often another man's disaster. A mild stress for A can overwhelm B. Take Mike, for example. Older than Jim, he had graduated from college two years ago. One Friday night he ran into a very attractive girl in one of the city's singles bars. One thing led to another and they ended up having dinner together.

When the check came, Ann opened her purse and started fumbling through it.

"What are you looking for?" Mike frowned.

"My wallet."

"Come on! This is on me."

"Why should it be?" She looked at him squarely.

"Hey, what are you? A women's lib kook?"

She found her wallet and snapped her purse shut. "I just want to pay my own way." She was beginning to get angry.

"I don't let girls pay when I take them out."

"Well, this girl does. I don't want to owe any guy anything."

Furious, Mike said, "Believe me, if I knew you were that up-tight I'd never have asked you out. You're not all that great to look at."

Ann slapped a ten-dollar bill on the table and in a loud voice said, "That covers dinner and drinks. If you don't like it you know what you can do!" She grabbed her coat and stormed out of the restaurant.

Mike paid the smiling waiter and scowled. "What the hell's so funny?"

"Hey man, don't take it out on me!"

By now Mike was boiling. He left furiously and on the way back to the apartment he thought of all the things he should have told Ann and the waiter. That night he was restless and uneasy, and he woke up half a dozen times.

He felt miserable for the entire weekend, and he called in sick on Monday. "I feel miserable," he told his boss. "My stomach hurts and I've got this terrible headache. I think I'm coming down with something."

The something he was coming down with was a typical severe anxiety attack. It seemed all out of proportion to the incident, a girl walking out on him, but it had triggered something in Mike. Unconsciously he related it to his mother's death when he was a child.

He had also linked it to a rejection at work a few weeks ago and to a dozen other seemingly unrelated events. They all acted on each other to build up that peculiar physical illness that comes from too great a load of anxiety.

All of us react to stress with different degrees of anxiety, but all of us also approach our anxiety differently. Some of us, like Mike, have to cope with it before it destroys us. Others, like Jim and Edith, use anxiety itself as a push to get going. Obviously, we would all be better copers if we could maneuver our anxiety into a push instead of a problem.

Jim and Mike are at opposite ends of the anxiety spectrum. If you lined up all the people in between, people who experienced every different degree of anxiety and asked them how it affected them, you'd get a variety of responses from "I feel uncomfortable, uneasy" to "I'm too sick to stand up. I threw up my meal. I just can't do anything."

And as for managing or coping with anxiety, again there is a tremendous range from "I'll feel better when I do it" to "My God, I'll never, never finish it—what am I going to do?"

THE STRESS OF CONFLICT

In spite of the musical *Hair*'s brave message, "This is the dawning of the age of Aquarius," for the better part of this century we've been living in the age of anxiety, and it doesn't promise to get any better. Our lives are made up of dozens of little incidents that seem tailored to make us anxious. Small stresses build up to greater ones; prices go up as employment goes down. The world seems engulfed in war, the cities in crime. Our values falter and our children bad mouth us while our parents reject us. Stress nips at our heels like a pack of hungry hyenas. And to make things worse, there are other stresses that gnaw at us from within.

"I live in constant dread," a friend told me recently. "I have a sense of foreboding, as if something terrible is going to happen."

"But why? What is it?" I asked.

He shook his head. "It's silly. I have my own ad agency, and I'm doing very well. My kids are great and I'm crazy about my wife—it doesn't make sense." He thought for a moment. "My parents were very religious, very moral. They never lied about anything, no matter how much the truth hurt, and you know, in my heart I still believe what they taught me."

"But you're not a liar. I know you."

"I'm not? Do you know how much I have to lie every day in my agency? The products I write copy about and don't believe in? The testimonials I conjure up? I couldn't put over a single presentation without faking and deceit!" He sighed. "Maybe that's what bothers me, but why should it make me feel so panicky?"

What my friend was feeling was the stress that comes from inside and is usually the result of a conflict. His parents' teachings were directly opposed to his work and he was aware of it. He couldn't give up his work because that would have deprived his family of so much. Nor could he give up his parents' morality. The head-on collision of the two had generated the growing anxiety that now threatened to panic him.

This conflict between morality and work often causes a disabling anxiety that we must cope with before we can cope with life. The soldier in battle, torn between fear of death and disloyalty to his comrades and country can feel the same stress and react with the same panic. It can paralyze him, blind him, or send him into an overwhelming depression.

In World War I they called it shell shock, thinking that the new and terrible shells caused mental concussion. In World War II it was combat fatigue or operational fatigue. Now it's labeled gross stress reaction, but the same old conflict causes it.

It's interesting that neurotic soldiers who know how to handle anxiety are less likely to suffer from stress reaction than men who haven't experienced anxiety in civilian life. Also, when the stress is mild, when the soldiers are not panicked but still afraid, they do a better job of soldiering. As one old army sergeant put it, "Give me a man who's smart enough to be scared. He'll be smart enough to do what he's told."

But coping better when we're scared doesn't apply only to soldiers. Chuck, a major league ballplayer, was always a little frightened and nervous in the dugout before a game. Once on the field, his uneasiness left him and he played like a dream. Chuck went through a seesaw reaction familiar to many of us. Before we set out to do a difficult job, we're keyed up and anxious. As we get into the job our tension disappears and we work all the better for it. It's like the stage fright actors get before the curtain goes up. It can help them give a smooth performance. Some of us are anxious before a test, but once we start we sail right through. The anxiety is just enough to tune us up, to get the best performance out of us.

THE ANXIETY OF CHILDHOOD

At what age does anxiety start? We know that little children feel it. Sometimes you can see it in their faces and in the tension of their bodies, but even before they understand what life is all about, before they talk or focus their eyes, babies react with anxiety. The latest thinking is that the very act of birth can start anxiety. With this in mind, a new style of childbirth suggests a quiet, darkened room for delivery, a birth with minimal stress, and an immediate, warm, relaxing bath for the baby. All this is designed to eliminate the anxiety of labor and birth—assuming it should be eliminated.

Does a newborn baby really react to stress with anxiety? Ask any mother. "When she hears a loud noise she catches her breath and her little hands just grab at the air. She shuts her eyes and after a few seconds lets loose with an awful scream."

What this mother describes is the classic "startle" response, and it ends with the baby coping with her fear. How? By crying. It's a universal coping method for babies. A good cry guarantees that mama will pick you up and comfort you.

That reassurance from mama is an important part of childhood coping. A child's security lies in the love and approval of her parents. This love and approval also reduces her anxiety. When Ginny is expected to play in her own backyard she does so and mama gives her approval. "You're a good girl. You stayed in the yard."

Ginny in turn feels secure, not because the yard is safe—she's really too young to understand about such safety—but because mama approves of what she did. If mama approved of her sneaking out and crossing the street through traffic, she'd do that, too, and feel secure.

In the same way Ginny's apprehension is reduced by mama's approval. Suppose she chases her ball out of the yard and mama finds out? Ginny is uneasy until mama says, "It's all right this time. You didn't go far and you came right back. You're a good girl."

Approval from a parent reduces a child's anxiety. In adulthood, your wife, your friends, your boss, the community all become approval-givers. As long as you have their blessing, you don't feel those butterflies in the stomach, that sinking feeling, that bothersome headache —whatever your body produces as a reaction to stress, and your body can really produce!

You can find yourself short of breath, your heart can start pounding, your mouth gets dry, your throat tight, and your appetite can go. Then there are the reactions you aren't even aware of. They occur because your body's autonomic nervous system rallies round to your body's alarm system. It's a primitive reaction, a holdover from the animal creature you once were.

Under stress, adrenalin is released into the blood, and this causes the liver to send out sugar which, in turn, supplies the muscles with quick energy. The heart beats faster in order to send the blood with its sugar and oxygen through the body. There's no need for sex or eating at a time like this, so these desires are inhibited as all systems hit go.

Although modern man rarely needs these "battle alarm" devices, he still reacts with them to even minor stress. As a result, the rapid heartbeat can be misdirected and can turn into palpitations. The adrenalin-sugar balance can be thrown off. The results can be troubling, confused, and even dangerous symptoms. Our reactions to stress can become overwhelming, and, instead of relieving our tension, increase it.

CALM OR WORRY: WHICH IS BETTER?

The stress that creates anxiety starts when we are born, and lasts all our life. Sometimes the anxiety is mild, as Jim's was; sometimes it's overwhelming like Mike's. Sometimes the stress that causes both reactions is the same, but different people manage their anxieties differently.

Ted was scheduled for a gall bladder operation in a neighborhood hospital. The night before the surgery, he assured his wife that he wasn't worried. "Hell, it's a routine thing, that's all."

When his surgeon came round to reassure him later that night, Ted shrugged his explanations away. "I'm in your hands, doc. I trust you. You take care of me."

Roger, in the next bed, had none of Ted's calm. He, too, was in for gall bladder surgery, but he told his brother who was visiting him, "Frankly, I'm scared. Oh, I need the operation. I can't go on with the pain I've been having, and I know that if they don't operate things will just get worse. Even if it hurts afterwards, and I know it will, believe me, I'm still going through with it."

After surgery Ted and Roger reacted differently. Ted was shocked by the postoperative pain. He had never expected it and he was angry about it. "I thought they were cutting me open to make me better. I never thought it would hurt this much. What kind of a deal is this?" His recovery was slow and his attitude resentful, as if he were being singled out for a particularly rough time.

Roger, on the other hand, experienced just what he expected and he was able to handle it with no trouble. In fact he was a model patient. He told his brother, "Sure it hurts. I told you it would, but it won't last long."

Roger had used his anxiety to rehearse his pain, and because of the rehearsal he was able to cope with it when it came. Ted, who wasn't at all anxious beforehand, was unequipped to handle his pain.

Like Roger, we can admit our anxiety in times of stress and use the admission to anticipate the trouble we'll face. It's a little like carrying an umbrella to cope with the rain. You're foolish if you carry it on a sunny day when no rain is expected, but you're wise if you take it with you when the sky is threatening.

COPING WITH LIMITATIONS

Even when we admit our anxiety, some of us can handle it and some of us can't. A recent study of a group of people with long-term disabilities makes this very clear. It cites the cases of Tony and Basil, two teen-agers who were both paralyzed after serious accidents. Tony was left with only a limited amount of hand movement; Basil was paralyzed from the waist down.

From the very beginning Basil refused to admit that he might not walk again, and he threw himself completely into the physical therapy program. His mother encouraged his efforts, also convinced that someday he would walk. But with all his efforts, the rehabilitation therapy just didn't work and eventually, depressed, Basil withdrew and refused any more treatment.

He wouldn't cooperate when a teacher came to the hospital to help him with his studies, and his depression grew worse. He began to feel pains that couldn't be accounted for, and he spent more and more time in bed.

After his discharge from the hospital, at his parent's urging, he finished high school, but he did nothing about finding a job. "When I'm able to walk again, I'll make plans," he told his parents stubbornly. "Just leave me alone."

Tony, more severely paralyzed, had been a basketball star in high school. He, too, kept hoping he'd walk and even play again, and his parents told him they believed he would. Still they made plans, "just in case." They built ramps in the house and widened doorways for his wheelchair.

Like Basil, Tony began by cooperating with the rehabilitation therapy. But, while he was still in the hospital, he finished his high school work. He, too, became depressed over his lack of improvement, but he didn't withdraw. Once out of the hospital, he considered a number of possible jobs. He thought of doing TV repair work, but finally admitted that his limited hand motion wouldn't permit it.

Eventually he settled for teaching, finished college, and became a high school history teacher and in his spare time coached a local boys club basketball team from his wheelchair.

Tony was able to cope with his paralysis—Basil never could. Basil would not accept the fact that he had changed physically. Tony did. "I'm not sick," he told his parents. "but now I'm a different person. I'm limited. Okay, I'll have to live with that. I have no choice, but damn it, I'll live up to my limitations!"

Both boys were put under the same type of stress—if anything Tony's was worse. The main difference between the two boys was self-recognition. Basil couldn't accept his new self. Tony did and respected it, and because of that respect he was able to cope.

BETTY FACES LIFE

A situation of terrible stress, like the paralysis these boys faced, can only be dealt with when it's accepted. By avoiding it, Basil saw only his limitations. By coping, Tony became aware of his potential as well as his limits.

The first thing you must understand when you cope with a major stress situation is that if you cannot change the stress, it becomes all-important how you handle the anxiety.

Sometimes avoiding the problem helps for a moment. It may make you feel better if you refuse to admit that something has gone wrong, or if you can laugh at it, or throw yourself into work in an attempt to forget it. But the problem won't go away, and in the long run you pay a price for avoiding it. Not only does the anxiety build up, even to the point where it can harm you physically, but you never learn how to solve the problem, or how to operate with the problem. You don't adapt to the new situation.

What you must do is face up to the problem, recognize your anxiety, and figure out a way to cope with it. Take Betty and her problem about a job.

When she graduated from college, Betty was afraid that she'd never find work in her field, medical editing. She had a number of interviews and to her complete astonishment two companies accepted her and offered her jobs within one week.

"I'm just flying," she told her parents. "Two jobs in one week. Oh, wow!"

But by the end of the day she was in the dumps again. "What am I going to do?" she asked them on the verge of tears. "What if I choose the wrong job? How can I tell which is right? Oh God, I don't want any supper. Please, I couldn't eat!" and she couldn't sleep either. She was up half the night in a panic.

By the next morning Betty knew she was at a crossroads in her life. The problem was not the two jobs, but how she'd handle the situation. She could either let her anxiety cripple her completely, as it threatened to do, or she could face the problem and take some sort of action.

Betty made a decision then and there and proceeded to "do something." She spent a day at each company and spoke to each personnel manager about benefits and increases, spoke to the supervisors, and compared the publications and projects. She spoke to other editors in both outfits and got their opinions.

Adding up what she learned, she had no trouble in making a decision. One company was head and shoulders above the other. The moment she made her mind up, she felt the tension drain out of her. She sealed her letter of acceptance and her letter of rejection and patted them both, then smiled at her parents. "I'll sleep like a baby tonight."

Betty laid her anxiety to rest by facing her problem and doing something about it, but this was only possible because she *could* do something. Often the problem is too overwhelming. It was that way with Tony. No amount of facing up to his paralysis would lessen it, but at least it helped him find a way to live with it.

No matter how terrible a problem is, the only way to relieve crippling anxiety is to face it squarely. If we can look a problem—and the anxiety it causes—straight in the face, it may not be as terrible as it seems, or if it is we may still be able to cope with it.

[CHAPTER TEN]

Weathering the Life Stress Crises

A CHARLIE IN OUR CLOSET

Stress teaches us to cope. The right amount nudges us along from day to day. A small problem makes us anxious, and the anxiety sharpens our coping ability. But sometimes the problems pile up, and anxiety mounts until we are out of our depths. We've reached a life crisis.

The contradiction about life crises is that even though they are times of overwhelming stress, they are also normal and predictable, and most people come out of them ahead of the game—a bit more knowledgeable about coping with life.

For all of those who can manage these crises, there are always a few who can't. Take Charlie. His parents call him a tennis bum. He's over thirty, but he hasn't a steady job. He always has a new girl, usually under twenty, and he spends his days on the tennis court. He's tan and muscular and good at the game, but not quite good enough to be a pro. Charlie's folks take care of him, and he doesn't need a job. They do it grudgingly, and there are periodic explosions, but none of it really touches Charlie. He's sailing into middle age, handsome, athletic, and very, very young.

Almost every family has a Charlie in the closet. If

he's not a son or a brother, he's a nephew or a cousin. No matter how old he is, he's still a kid, still unable to get his feet wet in the real world. Sometimes he's an athlete, sometimes a writer or a poet or a painter. Occasionally he's a businessman who never quite got started. Whatever he is, he's a victim of the second life crisis—adolescence. He's still caught in the debris of the years between 13 and 20.

Most psychologists agree that there are six major life crises:

1) Childhood: The years before 13.

2) Adolescence: From 13 to 20.

3) Adulthood: The time we start a career or job, get married, and become parents. Usually from 20 to the end of the 30s.

4) Middlescence: Turning 40 and entering middle age. From 40 to 60 for men and women.

5) The Climacteric: The menopause for women; the years around 50. For men, the failing of competence and sexual activity, retirement, the years around 65.

6) Separation: From retirement to death. A time of loss, of illness and the death of loved ones, of your own imminent mortality.

Some psychologists believe that there are more crises than these, some that there are less. Whatever the number, they are not always crises for everyone. Many people live through them without being aware that they've occurred. A few, like Charlie, become stuck in one period and never go on to the next. Some go through them long after their contemporaries do; some before.

SHELLY'S LIFE STRESS CRISIS

The first life stress crisis occurs during childhood. It is a crisis of separation, the start of school. The child is separated from her familiar world and placed in a strange, different, often frightening one. It is the first real adjustment she must make, if we discount birth itself. She must trade the security of her mother and her home for the unknown school, the strange teacher, and the alien children. She has no choice. She must go whether she wants to or not.

When five-year-old Shelly was told she would start kindergarten after the summer, she flatly refused. "I won't go. I just won't."

"Don't be silly," her mother told her. "It's going to be fun. You'll meet a lot of new children."

"They won't like me. I won't know anyone. They'll be mean to me!"

The first day of school Shelly threw a temper tantrum. When that didn't work, she vomited her breakfast on the school bus. Uneasily, as the bus drove off with her wailing daughter, Shelly's mother wondered if she hadn't started Shelly in school too soon. "She's so pathetic," she told her husband. "So forlorn on that bus—poor baby!"

"She'll straighten out. You'll see," her husband reassured her without much confidence.

But Shelly didn't straighten out, at least not for a long time. In fact she lost so much school work by being sick during the first four years that eventually she had to make up an extra term and move back to a class behind her own.

Surprisingly, this helped. "They're not such show-offs in this class," she told her mother. What she was really saying was that the competition was less. She had been through this same work the year before, and she was a little ahead of the class now and a lot more secure.

Shelly was a child who had enormous trouble getting over that first life stress crisis. There could have been many reasons for it. She may have started school when she was too immature. Perhaps she had never developed a sense of independence, or it may have been her mother's illness while Shelly was a baby. Whatever the cause, the result was an inability to cope with the first crisis of separation.

George, the boy who lived next door to Shelly and went to the same school at the same age, had a completely different experience. He couldn't wait to get to school. He had an older brother he envied who had been at school a year and a younger brother who annoyed him. School stood for freedom from his baby brother and equality with the older. George would play school for months before he actually went. He'd lay out his pencils and ruler on a desk in the playroom and then write the alphabet on a toy blackboard. "This is the way I'm going to do it in school," he'd say confidently. He was sure it would all be a wonderful time. He had no doubt that he'd make friends with the other children and the teacher.

George didn't say a word during his first day in school, but he watched everybody and everything with wide eyes and a serious face. That evening, when his mother asked him how he liked school, he said, "Oh yes, I liked it a lot. I want to go back."

George spent almost a week quiet and observant, absorbing everything, and then very slowly, but with confidence, he moved in and began to take part in things.

HOW TO COPE WITH TRANSITION

Shelly and George are two extremes, but almost every child approaches the strangeness of school with coping techniques that fit their own personalities, according to Dr. Lois Murphy in her study of childhood coping, *The Widening World of Childhood*. Some, like George, try to take in everything before they become a part of things. They use delay to size things up, often telling the teacher, "I'll do it when I feel like it."

There are some children who use flexibility as a coping tool in these early school experiences, and use it easily. They try everything out and decide how far they can go and what they can get away with. They test their limits, and if one activity isn't good they swing to another.

Other children must cling, almost desperately, to adults before they can take any independent steps. They beg their parents to stay with them, and they hold on to their mother's dress, her legs, or even to their teacher before mixing with the other children. Some children find the process of separation desperately hard and like Shelly, they fight it to the last minute. But unlike her, most adjust quickly once they realize they have no alternative. They mix with the other children and forget the reservations they had.

What makes the transition through this crisis easy for some children and so difficult for others? Why did George accept it so well while it almost destroyed Shelly? The clue lies somewhere in the background of each child. Shelly was an only child and overprotected. George came from a big family, but he also had his grandparents living next door. He had close ties to them as well as to his own father and mother. His parents were often too busy with his other brothers to give him the attention he wanted, so he'd go next door and get it from grandma and grandpa. It wasn't too hard for him to take the next logical step and expect to find attention and affection from his teacher.

Sometimes a new brother or sister can make the transition difficult. Molly's mother had a baby just a few months before Molly started school. Her new brother received so much attention that Molly became very uneasy about leaving the house.

"Will you be here when I come home?" was her constant question for the first month of school, and she would often run all the way home and burst into the house breathlessly. "To see my little brother," she'd explain, but it was to reassure herself that her mother hadn't gone off to the hospital again.

In Dr. Murphy's coping study, she found that the girl who was the youngest child in a family separated most easily from her parents. The boy who had severe difficulty with the transition was often one who had "erotically excited relations with his mother." Here the problem was as much the mother's doing as it was the child's. She would stop him on his way to school and ask, "Aren't you going to give me another kiss good-bye?"

Dr. Murphy makes the point that when mothering is too good, when babies have "excellent relationships" with their mothers, it is much harder to make the break from home to school. They can only accept a new situation if mother is there, too.

As confirmation, she cites the other side of the coin, a child whose mother was too involved with a new baby to give him excessive love. Because of this, new people and new experiences gave him the satisfaction he couldn't find with his own mother. Leaving the nest was no great effort.

A pattern begins to emerge. Children can be helped and strengthened while they are young so that when the first real life crisis comes, separation from home to enter school, they can cope with all the stresses involved. How do we help them?

By giving them independence.

By not overprotecting them.

By avoiding or minimizing their conflict with younger brothers or sisters.

By encouraging them, early in life, to make relationships with other adults besides their mother and father.

Some of these things can be done and some can't, but all parents should realize how much impact these things have on their children. They can affect the rest of the child's life, and the way he handles all the crises he will meet, not only as a child, but as an adult as well.

THE CASE OF THE FOUR TEEN-AGERS

The second life stress crisis is the period of adolescence. It isn't an easy period, this growing from child to adult. Hormones change the body, often before the child is ready for change. The voice deepens, the trunk thickens, and the face loses its dewy innocence. Sex is suddenly a force to be dealt with, and all manner of identity problems begin. Who am I? What am I? Where am I going?

The adolescent is torn between childhood and adulthood. Clinging to one, he's forced by his body and society toward the other, and the simplest questions can set off the wildest conflicts. Must I wear braces on my teeth? Will I ever get rid of my acne? Will my breasts develop? Must they be this big? How can I make them bigger? Why haven't I a beard yet? I hate this hair on my chest! Why don't I have hair on my chest? I'm too small, too big, too fat, too skinny . . .

And then there are parents who suddenly and unaccountably change from nurturing, understanding creatuers to demanding and critical monsters. "My dad drives me up a wall," Bill complains. "Nothing I do is right. He tells me I should be more of a man, make decisions for myself, and stop asking him what to do all the time. Okay, I try to do that, and what happens? He cuts me down!

"Like this great set of speakers. I see this crazy bargain, a hundred-dollar set for twenty-five bucks, and I take the money I've saved out of the bank and I buy it. It's my money and I've always wanted good speakers for my hi-fi. So does Dad say, 'Good boy. You got a smart bargain'? No way. He yells at me, 'Can't you hold on to money? Don't you know how important it is to keep a few bucks in the bank?'

"I can't tell him that music means more to me than money. No. Right away I'm a spendthrift. I can't handle money. I rush into things—then in the same breath he tells me to be independent!"

With incidents like this happening all the time, adolescence is one big crisis to Bill. With his friend Jeremy, things are different. Jeremy is able to cope with the whole situation. He even weathered that first break with home when he was put into kindergarten. It was rough, but he came through, and now he's safe and secure in the school system. His day-to-day problems create the same anxieties for Jeremy that they do for everyone else, but he's only driven to cope a little harder.

Tests, vacations, friendships, grades, honor roles—all of these have been minor problems, but now Jeremy is in his late teens and approaching that time of great adolescence. Whether he wants to or not, he's becoming a man. How will he take it?

Bill and Jeremy's classmate, Marcia, is changing, too, and becoming a woman, developing breasts and hips and going through a similar crisis. It's a rough time for all the kids of that age. They're learning to relate to each other. They are getting free of their parents so they can do their own thing, and a few are trying to discover who they are. They're dating, and some are discovering sex while the rest wish they could.

But for most of them the real crisis is like the one they went through in childhood, a crisis of separation. They have to leave home and make a break with their old way of life. Jeremy and Marcia are going off to college. Bill won't be able to. His family can't afford it. But he still must make the same break. He has to get out in the world, hunt for a job, find his own apartment, manage on his salary—and it all seems too much. He doesn't feel equipped for it, and he isn't sure he'll make it.

Elsie, Marcia's best friend, is in the same boat as Bill. She can't afford college. But Elsie has always worked. She held a job in the supermarket all through high school and she has no fears. She knows she'll find work, and she intends to take any job while she tries for beautician's school. "There's a lot of money in it," she tells Marcia. "Eventually I figure to open my own place."

Jeremy finds it a problem to select a college. Will it be the right one? To get passing grades. Will they be high enough for acceptance? To pass the college entrance exams, to go through all the application details. But hard as all these chores are, he manages to do them and do them well. Marcia, however, finds the same chores overwhelming and she only manages because her parents and teacher take over and do most of the work for her. Even then, she leaves for college tense and apprehensive.

But anyone knowing the backgrounds of all these young people could guess how they would cope. Jeremy has always coped successfully, and nothing succeeds like success. He simply expects things to work out well, and they do. Elsie is like that, too. She always worked and work held no threat for her. Bill had never worked before, and he had no idea of how to go about getting a job. Marcia always had trouble coping, and she knew that things in college would be no different. When she finally graduated from college the same crisis was repeated. Leaving the security of campus life and going out into the real world was too much. She went through a typical life crisis and handled it badly. She finally went back to school, graduate school, not to learn more but simply to avoid facing life.

Jeremy, on the other hand, looked forward to graduating from college. He knew what he wanted to do and he had been exploring the job market for months. He couldn't wait for his diploma. His graduation was no crisis but the beginning of a promising future.

The same question arises again when we consider these four adolescents. Why do different people react differently to the same stresses? The obvious answer is because of their differences, but what makes those differences? What coping tools does an adolescent use to handle a situation competently?

CAROL'S COMPETENT COPING

Dr. George V. Coelho, Behavioral Science Coordinator of the Research Task Force at the National Institutes of Mental Health has been intrigued with just this question. In a series of studies, he and his associates have explored different aspects of coping behavior in adolescent development and have tried to describe how competent adolescents cope with one of the problems of the second life crisis—going off to college.

His method was to choose a number of students who had coped successfully with their academic work, with their friendships, and with their social activities. He examined their coping methods in long searching interviews.

One fact that emerged from Dr. Coelho's study was that most of these top students went on to college, not because they had decided to go on their own, but because their parents expected it. So did the school and the community. The parents usually had definite ideas about which school they thought their children should attend, and they let them know how they felt.

In most cases the children went along with their parent's suggestions, but the parents didn't put up a fight when the children decided to go somewhere else. If money was a problem, the children looked for scholarships, or part-time jobs.

Children who coped well had a good family relationship. They respected their family's wishes, and the family respected theirs. That was obvious. But what are successful adolescent copers like? If we study them, can we learn something to help our own children cope? Or to help us cope?

Carol, a composite of Dr. Coelho's successful high school senior, seems to sum it all up. She's an attractive girl and fun to be with. "College should be great," Carol says. "Meeting new people is cool, and I like new experiences. I really dig change, and I'll be on my own. That's exciting."

About her roommate-to-be, Carol shrugs. "So she's a complete stranger. That's great. I mean, it'll be fun rooming with someone different, maybe even from a new state. Sally, she's my best friend, is going to the same college, but we agreed not to room together. It'll be cool having her around, but like we've known each other a long time. She'll still be my friend, but I want to make new friends, too."

Her mother wondered if Carol would get along with her roommate. "Remember when Joanne came up from Texas and stayed with us?" Carol asked. "Well, we got along okay. I mean, she had her problems, but it was still fun having her in my room. Don't worry."

Carol shopped for her own college clothes, did her own packing, planned her own college program, and made arrangements with her parents to open a checking account at the college town. "I can handle my money."

About her schoolwork, Carol said, "I always enjoy problems. I love solving them and learning new things. It's like meeting new people." She also pointed out that going off to college "is just another step on the ladder. It's not like jumping off. I mean, it's time I grew up anyway."

Carol prepared for college by learning as much as she could about the school she selected, and also by rehearsing her role as a college freshman, reading books she knew would be required that first year, learning to arrange her clothes the way they would be in her room at school, and even taking the hardest courses available in her senior year in high school. "To get used to college-level work, you know."

Carol's personality is that of an adolescent who copes well, who uses not one but all the available coping tools and so handles each life crisis with ease. Partly it's because she refuses to see them as crises, but instead looks at them as times of change, exciting times.

She also considers herself adequate to any new situation. If there's any doubt, she points to other changes in her life that she handled easily. "If I could do it then, I'll be able to do it next time."

Carol responded to the stress brought on by the rites of passage from high school to college by coping. She wanted to go on to the next challenge, and for that reason she considered a crisis no more than a challenge.

Again the pattern of creative coping emerges:

1) See change as something exciting.

2) Cite past success as a pattern for the future.

3) Expect the best in new experiences.

4) Be autonomous. Be your own person. Make your own decisions. Take your own responsibilities. Handle your own affairs.

5) Rehearse expected problems and work out the solutions in advance.

[CHAPTER ELEVEN]

From the Tranquil Twenties to the Threatening Thirties

LIVING HAPPILY EVER AFTER

We meet our third life crisis as we pass into the thirties, right smack in the middle of that long climb from twenty to forty. We've come through adolescence and made our break with home, or failed to. We've made some tentative choices for the future, but we've neglected to ask a few crucial questions such as *Where are we going? What does it all mean?* or *What is our ultimate goal?*

Who has time for questions like that at twenty? Right now we're too eager to enter the adult world. We're fully grown, our bodies at peak efficiency, our minds at their keenest. The world is our oyster, young and fresh and waiting for us. What are we going to do about it?

This chapter tells the story of four people who made the transition from adolescence to adulthood and whose lives, at one point or another, crossed each other's. Three of them, Sandy, Elaine, and Mercedes, were art students. The fourth, Alex, was a college dropout.

Mercedes, who wanted to be a sculptor, found the transition to adulthood hard. She had asked herself some searching questions, and had decided to keep her integrity, even if it meant making no commitments.

Sandy and Elaine, on the other hand, had no doubts

or questions about their lives. They were going to live happily ever after. Why not? They had fallen in love while still students, while Sandy was studying commercial art and Elaine wanted to be a painter. "And you're damn good," Sandy told her one afternoon in the studio, looking over her work. "You've got a fantastic color sense."

Elaine protested. "But you've got real technique. Your work is so smooth."

"Commercial," he corrected her. "Well, it better be if I'm going to support the two of us."

"Just like that," Elaine remembered later. "A typical Sandy proposal!"

They were married right after graduation, and that summer Sandy got a job with an advertising agency. They rented an apartment in an old Victorian house and settled down to married life. Elaine set up a little studio in the extra room, and for a year she kept up her painting, with Sandy's encouragement. Then Judy was born, and fifteen months later, Tim.

"What the hell would Van Gogh have done if he had to lug two kids around?" she asked Sandy ruefully. "Motherhood is incompatible with art!"

Sandy kissed her. "Are you sorry?"

"Regretful, maybe, but never sorry."

She put her canvasses away in a closet with a sigh. It was a good marriage, and where was it written that a woman had to be creative? Wasn't being a wife and mother creative enough?

Looked at objectively, Sandy and Elaine's life seemed happy. Surely there was not enough stress to create any serious life crisis. In five years they moved into their own house. Sandy was made creative art director at the office and he began teaching a class at the art institute. The children were healthy and happy. Elaine had friends in the neighborhood, a lovely house, a successful husband—it had to be the best happy-ever-after yet.

Still, with all of this, the tranquility of their lives began to heave and buckle as the fateful thirties approached. It started with Sandy.

"I don't know," he told his friend. "I just don't feel that Elaine has grown. What with the kids and the house —her horizons are so damned limited. There seems to be less and less we can talk about."

"But she's an artist, too, isn't she?" his friend asked.

"She's a wife and mother. Period!"

Inevitably, Sandy met a young woman in the art department who offered the excitement and understanding he needed, whose talk didn't revolve around children, home, and cooking. She had taken his class and found something brilliant in his lectures. Admiration led to respect and love, and very soon after, sex.

"Christ, it's like being born again," Sandy told his friend in confidence. "I had forgotten what the whole thing was about."

"And Elaine?"

"Whatever we felt for each other is dead. She was never all that keen about sex anyway," Sandy said and really believed it.

Elaine, however narrow her viewpoint, was no fool. She realized that Sandy had found another woman. She tried to hold the marriage together, but it didn't work. "Whatever I do," she told her friend Mercedes, "all I seem to accomplish is extra guilt and unpleasantness. I feel cheated and—oh God, betrayed! And I don't know what I want. I've devoted ten years to Sandy and what have I got? If I hire a lawyer I'll have the kids and alimony. Big deal!"

"At least it's something," Mercedes said.

But Elaine saw only one thing. Sandy wanted to get rid of her. He had used her when he needed her, but now she was too limited. Well, whose fault was that? She had given up her painting for him. She had been a good wife, a devoted mother.

Elaine has reached her life stress crisis, in fact has been brutally pushed into it, and has no tools to cope with it. She can try to patch up her marriage, hating and loving Sandy, but he doesn't need a mother-wife figure now. He needs a stimulating, exciting companion, and she can't make the grade.

MERCEDES: HER OWN WOMAN

When Mercedes leaves Elaine she shakes her head in bewilderment. She thought Elaine had it made, a husband, a home, children—all the things Mercedes had denied herself.

Mercedes had graduated from art school with Sandy and Elaine, but from the very beginning her life was different. Mercedes despised material possessions and long-term goals. She wanted to be her own woman and not get locked into any life role.

After school she rented a loft downtown and deliberately picked jobs with no future. She was a waitress, a department store clerk, a typist, and even a hatcheck girl —anything to earn enough bread to make it. "I want to sculpt, and all I need is money enough for materials, food, and the rent."

Elaine was the only friend Mercedes kept from the old days. She shrugged off her other classmates. "They've all become fat cats in the system. They've sold out."

"Like me?" Elaine would smile.

Mercedes would shrug. "You were a damned good colorist. You should have kept at it, even if you had to starve."

Mercedes' life had no permanent men in it. The ones she slept with came and stayed a while and left. She kept sculpting and eventually built up enough of a reputation, sold enough of her work through a few small shows to give up her other jobs.

When she was twenty-eight Mercedes had an affair that wasn't as easy to shrug off as the others. She lived with Jack for two years and had a baby. They were married and then separated, and at thirty Mercedes was left with the child and a fistful of bitterness. Now she wondered if her life was so different from Elaine's. But at least she had her work. She had always known just what she wanted out of life and she went after it. As a woman, she felt she had to give up the establishment and a family to get it, but in the end her affair with Jack had betrayed her—or was it betrayal? She had her child and her work. What did Elaine have?

YOUR PLACE OR MINE?

Alex, another sometime-friend and sometime-lover of Mercedes, had also faced a life stress crisis at thirty. He had gone to high school with Mercedes and then he had gone on to the university to take a pre-med course. After two semesters he decided against medicine and dropped out in his second year.

Alex's relationship to Mercedes was a very casual one. "I can't really stick around any place or girl for long," he told her, explaining that it was just the way he was. The way he was went beyond emotional commitments. He couldn't stick to any job for long either. He had no real occupation. He took whatever work he could get, and stayed with it only as long as he needed the money. He gradually drifted into the singles scene, finding his women in bars and taking them to his place or going to theirs for impersonal, one-night stands.

When he did meet someone he liked, he backed away in a hurry. "I don't want to be tied down. I don't want to spoil this by letting it get serious. You make a friend and you have a friend to lose. No thanks, I'm a loner."

But at thirty, still without a steady job or any direction to his life, Alex panicked. He met Ruth in a singles bar, and she seemed more intelligent, more of a person, more together than any of the other girls he had taken home.

"It was like I woke up that morning and went to the sink to shave and I looked at myself in the mirror and said, 'Jesus Christ! Am I Peter Pan? Am I never going to grow up?' I could see all the years in my face, my receding hairline, the creases around my eyes, the beginning of jowls. I asked myself, 'What am I doing? Where am I going? What do I want out of life?' "

Alex married Ruth, running into the marriage scared, without thinking or listening to anyone's advice or paying any attention to Ruth's doubts. "Then and there I decided it was going to work. I was going to get a steady job and grow up fast!"

THE CRISES WE CAN HANDLE

These are four different lives, and they typify four common reactions to the life stress crisis that takes place at thirty, the passage from the twenties. This isn't the only crisis of adulthood. Marriage, starting a career, becoming parents are all stressful situations, and yet we can usually cope with them. It is the age transition and all it symbolizes—the loss of youth, missed chances, a hint of mortality—that usually precipitates a major life crisis and makes coping so difficult.

For most adults, marriage is normal and expected in the early twenties, but even so the change from one to two is often hard to take. Before marriage Sandy had only himself to think about. He had his own problems, his own likes and dislikes to handle. He could see the people he wanted to and avoid those he didn't. Marriage made a big difference.

To begin with there was the sexual adjustment. Before, if sex didn't work out, he would look for a new partner. Now he had Elaine, for better or worse. There were also the constant adjustments you had to make when you lived with another person.

As for Elaine, she had to put aside her painting even before the children came. Marriage taught her her real devotion had to be to Sandy and the children. She had to learn to keep house, to be a wife and mother, and to get along with Sandy's family and friends.

Sandy had similar adjustments, true, but he had his career to compensate him. For many people the start of a career can be a crisis in itself, but in Sandy's case the job fulfilled so many of his personal needs that it helped him grow. Taking on responsibility at work made him more sure of himself, more capable.

He and Elaine had agreed, early in their marriage, that they didn't have to share everything. Sandy had his poker night with the boys, his squash game on Sunday morning, his late, late movies, and Elaine had her painting, her lecture series at the museum, and her long walks around the lake. These were some of the things they didn't share with each other. It worked at first because there was so much they did share.

Parenthood shifted everything and could have become a life crisis, but they coped with it. The baby ate up Elaine's free time and there was no more painting, no more solitary walks. They couldn't go out together whenever they wanted to. There were baby-sitters, formulas, diapers to attend to.

In fact, while the coming of the children was not, in itself, a crisis, it contributed to the eventual crisis they both went through. Elaine became more and more child-oriented, overprotective. She limited her social life so she could be close to the children, and Sandy resented this. He turned more and more to his job while Elaine's world centered around the children and home.

Sandy's reaction wasn't unusual. Fatherhood can put as much of a stress on men as motherhood does on women. Dr. Roy Lacoursier, staff psychiatrist at the Menninger Foundation, reported recently that the stress of fatherhood can cause symptoms varying from mild nausea and vomiting to severe gastrointestinal distress, sexual deviation, and outright psychosis. "It forces a shift or change in the way a man usually behaves," he said. "His wife becomes more concerned with herself and less with her husband. She is usually less sexually responsive."

THE THREATENING THIRTIES

With Alex and Mercedes, both single until close to thirty, the situation was different. Mercedes went through a minimal life crisis when she graduated from art school. Her decision was to cope by avoiding marriage and a family. More than anything, she wanted to fulfill herself, to do her thing, but not in the careless, do-nothing sense of many young people. She wanted to sculpt and she didn't want to commercialize her work. If it was good and received critical acclaim, fine. If it was bad and nobody bought it, she still intended to keep at it.

It was only when she hit thirty and found herself with a baby and no husband that she came face-to-face with a real life crisis.

Alex, on the other hand, was a life transient until he hit thirty, a man totally without commitment. He didn't go through the mini-crises of a career, marriage, or fatherhood, and when his life stress crisis occurred at thirty he had no previous experience in coping to help him. Of the four, Alex should have had the most disastrous life. His marriage was based on panic. He had never shared his life with anyone, never tried to make a career for himself, nor tried to accept responsibility for anything. And yet, oddly enough, Alex coped very well with his life crisis.

Once married he felt a tremendous need to settle down and become a solid citizen. "I've done the single bit for too many years. I know what that scene's all about, and what a trap it is. Now I want everything I've never had, a wife, a family, a home, and above all, a steady job."

Born out of his panic, Alex's coping skills emerged at thirty and he began to establish his commitment to life. His marriage has been successful, and he made one last job switch, this time with some planning, into a field he liked. Within five years he became a respectable partner in the firm. He has one child now, and more than a moderate amount of satisfaction.

"I don't feel restless in my marriage because I know what it's like to be alone. I've been there!"

Sandy hasn't. He's been locked into a marriage since he became a man, and now, at the life crisis of thirty, he makes a sudden decision to tear apart the fabric of the life he so carefully put together and try to make a new one with the young woman from the art department.

"There has to be something else besides this. My marriage is a laugh. I've grown so far ahead of Elaine it isn't funny. I have nothing in common with her except the kids. My real life is out there, the job, the people I see every day. My home and my wife are anchors, that's all. I've got to cut loose or drown."

And he cuts loose to find himself. It's the only way he can cope with the overwhelming crisis of thirty.

And Elaine? At first the divorce devastates her. She devoted her life to her marriage and now it all falls apart. Where can she turn? What can she do? She must relearn all the skills she has forgotten, how to become one out of two, an individual, how to relate to men, how to earn a living—and still be a mother.

Gradually Elaine fights through the crisis because

she has no choice. She emerges as something she's never been in all her years of marriage, a woman in her own right. She finds a job and with her alimony manages to get through. But more important to herself, she resurrects her canvasses from storage and sets up a studio and begins to work again.

"It's as if I were only twenty," she tells Mercedes. "I feel I'm just learning how to live, like all those years spent as only a mother and housewife I existed in a cotton cocoon, except that I didn't develop into a goddamned butterfly! I came out the same dud I went in, and now I've got to start all over again. And yet, I'm not sorry it all happened. Oh, I'm unhappy about Sandy and the mess of our marriage, but I'm discovering that I shouldn't have ever stopped growing and developing as a person."

But Elaine had to stop. What she overlooks is that when a woman accepts the role of wife and mother she gives up the ability to grow as her husband grows. She develops in another direction, as a wife and mother. If she enjoys it, fine—providing that it can continue, that her husband doesn't grow along a path she cannot follow, that a life stress crisis doesn't smash the whole thing to bits.

Of the four whose lives we followed, Merecedes probably found it hardest to cope with her crisis. She had her baby and raised her alone. She had never separated herself from life, and the years after thirty were no discovery for her. She coped as she had coped before. She continued to sculpt and to live the life she had always lived, free and open.

"But it's always been this way for me," she told Elaine. "I envy you discovering freedom now and learning to become a whole person. I've always been free and I am whole. Maybe that's good, but good or bad, I have to cope!"

AFTER THE THIRTIES

The crises of the thirties over, we usually subside with a sigh, a gasp, or a whimper, into the next decade. This is a time of settling in, of sending out roots. If we have been rebels against our parents or the system, these are the years when we sell out the revolution and come over to join the Establishment. We give up the far-out clothes, the souped-up cars, the restless itches, and we suddenly rediscover basic truths, good old values, our parents' wisdom, society's good points.

Some of us give up the rebellion reluctantly, knowing that no real victory was ever possible. Others are truly converted and look back at their early years with a touch of wonder. Did I do that? Was I that crazy? What was I trying to prove?

If their marriage has worked out and husband and wife have grown together, they may now find themselves allied against their own children as they approach the crisis of adolescence. The husband is now integrated into the business community, accepting the uniform of his job, the coloration of his peers, flattening out his political views. This is the time when many men go into business for themselves.

As comfortable as his marriage is, he now begins to fret within its confines. Is this all there is? Who is this woman I'm living with?

For the married woman, these years are often confused. The active mothering role she took during her twenties is changing. If she had her children by twenty-five, they have grown into independence when she's in her mid- and late-thirties, and she suddenly becomes aware that they will need her less and less from now on.

She may cope by turning more to her husband as

the ties with the children weaken, or she may attempt to tighten those ties, to become more possessive, more of a mother, more demanding.

Many women, realizing that the family unit they've known is about to break up, will try to shake the role of mother and get out into the real world again. In their late thirties they will go back to school, look for a job, or try their hand at the creative arts.

The conflict arises now because the husband is settling into his role and accepting the way of life he once resisted. He has found the compensation and stimulation he needs outside his home during the years his wife was busy with the children. Now that she has shaken loose, he finds it hard to accept her bid for independence. This isn't the woman who's been such a good housekeeper all these years. What does she want of him?

To accept her, he has to turn away from any outside commitments he's made—the other woman, the friends in business, the business itself, the job—and come home to her to join up with her life again.

This is a difficult and sometimes impossible transition to make, and it usually comes when he is approaching the age of forty, a time of added trauma and stress, when he has sailed through the tranquil twenties, weathered the threatening thirties, and is headed for the reefs and shoals of the frantic forties.

Is there anything we can learn from the way these four handled their life crises? A few suggestions seem obvious:

1) Ask yourself what you want out of life at twenty instead of at thirty, and make sure you answer the question.

2) If you're a woman, don't allow yourself to be completely submerged in home and children. Try to keep other options open, and if you're a man, decide which is the most important part of your life—family or job. If it's a job and a career, you have no business being

married. If it's at least fifty-fifty, devote that much time to each.

3) Watch out for that fateful drift apart after the kids come.

4) Make sure you're cut out for domesticity before you try it. If you're not, make some arrangement with your mate. No children or hired help from the beginning.

5) Remember that you can come out of a life stress crisis stronger than when you went in—and better able to cope with life.

[CHAPTER TWELVE]

Guidelines for Middlescence

THE DANGEROUS AGE

"I had no trouble when I hit forty," Tom told his younger brother. "I don't see why it should be such a problem for you. It seems to me I sailed right through it."

His wife, Rhoda, smiled. "You've forgotten, dear. That was the year you lost twenty-five pounds and bought contact lenses."

"Oh, well . . ." Uncomfortably, Tom shrugged that off. "I had a new job, and you have to look your best when you're out selling."

Afterwards, in the kitchen, Rhoda told her sister-in-law, "Whatever Tom says, turning forty is a rough time. You have to treat them with kid gloves."

Her sister-in-law nodded. "I'm finding that out."

As she put the silver away, Rhoda said carefully, "That was the year he got mixed up with that hostess at the Ramada Inn—a silly kind of stunt." She bit her lip and her sister-in-law nodded. "I remember. Yes, I guess it's a rough time."

Though Tom himself had forgotten, or had pretended to forget, his fortieth year had been traumatic. His greatest trouble was an identity problem, the sort of thing many young people go through in their adolescence. As he told Rhoda at the time, "I don't know who I am anymore. I look in the mirror when I get out of the shower, and there's this fat old man staring back at me! What the hell has happened?"

What has happened, happened gradually over the years, and it had never bothered Tom. It was only when he suddenly awoke to the realization that he was at the midpoint of his life, that the odds were all that he had already lived more than half the time allotted to him, that he plunged feet first into a life stress crisis.

Tom's is not an unusual case. He dealt with it by losing weight, by getting contact lenses, trying to recapture the image of the man he once was, by changing his job to prove he could still make it in a new field and, of course, by trying to prove to himself that he could still function sexually. The most obvious way to do this was to have an affair outside of his marriage.

Medical statistics show that during the fortieth year and shortly after, men have more sexual problems, more divorces, succumb more often to alcoholism and suicide, have more accidents and heart attacks, ulcers and high blood pressure than ever before.

They become restless, dissatisfied with the way their life is going and frightened that somehow, in some way, they are being left behind. It may be only time that's doing them in, but they see it as their entire life-style. Suddenly their work becomes dull and pointless and they're less efficient, less satisfied with what they're accomplishing. Like Tom, many try to retailor their images, and many of them change their jobs, not necessarily for something better, but often just for the change.

MIDDLESCENCE

Like adolescence, this period has been referred to by psychologists as middlescence, a time of minor upheaval and anxiety. While the young adolescent is discovering sex for the first time, his middlescent counterpart is rediscovering it. Sometimes he finds it with his own wife, but more often than not, he has to look somewhere else for it.

Not all men in middlescence are able to reassure themselves of their own sexuality or their importance in the world. Many see themselves pushed out by younger men. They become acutely aware that they are rushing toward obsolescence. They have an intimation of their own mortality and they can become seriously depressed.

Alfred went through a typical life stress crisis at forty, and he took it hard. His work suffered, his marriage was strained, he couldn't get along with his children, and he'd sink into long, moody periods for no apparent reason. Eventually, at his wife's urging, he went to his family doctor for some medical help.

"What you're going through is common to most men at your age," his doctor reassured him. "Your health is good. Your heart is fine. You're a little flabby and I'd recommend exercise—but there's no real problem."

"But that's just it," Alfred protested. "There is a problem." He hesitated a moment. "Maybe it's time. I get so damned depressed when I realize its running out."

Trying not to be impatient—he had a busy schedule and a waiting room full of patients—the doctor closed Alfred's folder. "We all feel that. Well, it's running out for all of us. Look, let me give you something to tide you over, something to relax you."

Reluctantly Alfred took the prescribed tranquilizer, but at work the next day he watched his dynamic boss handle a minor business crisis and he thought, "It's not true that everyone feels this. Vernon there is my age, and there isn't a hint of depression or doubt about him. How does he do it?"

Vernon, on his part, after a morning of tough decisions, a critical business lunch, and a tense meeting in the afternoon, called his wife in the suburbs to tell her he'd be a bit late, left the office early and spent two hours in one of the city's best hotels with Millie Shelton, a very expensive call girl his firm used from time to time for out-of-town clients.

Vernon, for all his dynamic front, suffered the same mid-life crisis as his employee, Alfred. He handled it differently. His own doubts about his sexual ability were assuaged by Millie. His other problems, the tension of having to keep up the image of a top executive, his health, the fact that he and his wife were drifting apart, his doubts about whether financial success was all that important—all these typical stresses of the transition from the thirties to the forties were still there, still tearing away at him and producing a mid-life crisis. But he coped with all of it by concealing everything.

THE EXECUTIVE SYNDROME

The Menninger Foundation, aware of this problem because of their involvement with top-level management, has created an organization called the Life Management Assessment Center. It was set up specifically to deal with the problems of executives faced with middlescence.

The foundation has come to the conclusion that one of the prime reasons that such executives go through their mid-life crisis is the strain of concealing their problems. To admit them would place them in a vulnerable position and take away their ability to handle the men under them. Executives, then, are not only stressed by the same problems we all pass through at forty, but their stress is compounded by the need to conceal it.

Alfred could let his family see how troubled he was. He could complain to his doctor and even to Vernon, his boss, as a last resort. Vernon might suggest a few weeks off to get things together. But Vernon himself had no one to confide in. Even Millie, the call girl, was less a confidante than a means of reassurance, a symbol that life wasn't passing him by.

We all need such reassurance, and all of us cope with this period of crisis by searching for it. Vernon could afford a call girl. Men who can't may look for an available woman, a secretary at work, a waitress where they have lunch—or they may reduce it all to flirtation and find a willing airline stewardess, a friend of the family, a neighbor.

Some men have a sudden awareness that their own self-image doesn't match up to what the mirror shows. Their identities are frozen in a time past when they were young and attractive. Now they find that the reality is older, fatter, balder. They cope by changing their style of clothes, by trying to send out a different body message with pants and shirts and suits. "Look at me. I'm still young, still in the running."

This is a great age for hair pieces, hair grafts, long sideburns, and beards. Teeth are capped, skins are tanned, weight is lost, and jogging, tennis, swimming are suddenly popular.

What is needed, in a coping sense, is a marshaling of all the available coping tools, a sense of ambiguity to realize what options are open, a sense of flexibility, particularly emotional, to invest meaning to new activities, relationships, and experiences.

There must be an awareness that while life has reached a midpoint, it hasn't reached an endpoint. There are still changes to come, new developments, new things to learn. The frantic attempts to change their image, look for new sexual stimulation, new jobs, should be toned down to a realistic level.

A new job may be a good idea, but at this age change for the sake of change alone is foolish. There is nothing wrong with changing one's image; it can wake you up to the reality of change, to the understanding that life goes on. As for sexual stimulation, while this is important, it can be found within an old relationship as easily as outside it. Forty is a good time to rediscover the romance of a marriage, to court your wife again, and to rediscover your own sexual potential.

It is also an age when many men finally come to grips with the truth of their own sexuality. A psychiatrist reports that this is the age when many men, boxed into the wrong sexuality, shake free.

As a case in point, take Barry. Married for fifteen years and the father of two children, at forty he suddenly confesses to his wife that he is basically homosexual, that he has had affairs throughout his marriage, and now he can no longer live a lie. He's met a man he wants to share his life with.

His announcement is devastating to his wife, but it is no less an act of coping than Harry's announcement to his wife, at the same age, that he has met another woman and she offers him all the things his own marriage lacks. He wants his freedom.

Or Larry, who copes by continuing in his marriage, but meeting other women for brief, passionate affairs that always end with, "I can't leave my wife and children. I don't dare."

Each, in his own way, copes with his changing sexual needs, and copes at an age of crisis.

A PAUSE OR AN END?

These are all men, and it sometimes seems as if the mid-life crisis is a peculiar part of the male problem. Certainly it seems more of a blow to the male ego. But this is only because women have been through the same sort of stress earlier in their thirties when the children leave home for school. But if they seem to escape unscathed at forty, it is only to head straight into the period of the menopause, those years from forty-five to fifty.

It's a part of the general economy of nature that a woman's ovaries not only produce egg cells, but also the hormones that keep her body fit and her psyche in good shape. It's also nature's wastefulness that at the menopause, when they stop producing eggs, the ovaries also stop producing hormones. In these years, as the production slows down and finally stops, a woman is subject to the internal stress of adjusting to a new hormonal system. She is also faced with the outside stresses that can plunge her into a full-scale life stress crisis.

This is the time of the empty nest syndrome, but it is also a time when her husband has made his peace with his own life crisis and has settled into that long, productive plateau before retirement.

Marianne had never troubled herself about age. She was one of those good-looking women who seem to grow more attractive as they grow older. When she and her husband reached forty, she watched his identity struggle with some sympathy, but mostly with humor. "There are some things you can't fight, like city hall and growing old," she told him, and she genuinely believed it.

But when she hit her menopause, she tooks things very hard. "I don't know what it is," she told her friend. "You seemed to go through it with no trouble, but I find it just terrible. Aside from the hot flushes, I get tired so easily. I have no energy, and all I do is think about it and I come down with a cold, but what bothers me most—" she shivered a little, "I feel so vulnerable."

"Vulnerable?"

"Yes. Every wrinkle seems to stand out. Every gray hair is so obvious. My arms, my neck—I pick up a magazine and look at the fashions and I realize that I'm such a hag. I'm old, old!"

Her friend shook her head. "Good Lord, there are things you can do. You don't have to dress your age. I have my hair done every month, and there's still plastic surgery—no one has to grow old, Marianne."

But later, looking at herself in the bedroom mirror, Marianne asked her husband, "Would you like it if I had my hair done?"

"Done? What do you mean?"

"You know. To get rid of the gray."

"Dye your hair? Why the hell should you?" He snorted and went back to his book. "At your age!"

But what is my age, Marianne asked herself. I'm almost fifty. Does that mean I throw in the sponge? Get granny shoes and dresses that hide my upper arms? Do I go gray and give up makeup?

In a world that caters to youth, Marianne faced a typical dilemma. She didn't feel old or think old, but somewhere along the line nature had let her down. She *was* old. How could she possibly cope with that?

Not every woman who enters the menopause finds it a terrifying or even disturbing time. Some look on it as a relief from thirty years of bother and discomfort and the fear of pregnancy. As one woman put it, "Now my husband is a freedom rider!"

A recent report in *Psychosomatic Medicine* indicated that most postmenopausal women across the country had few crying spells or bouts of irritability, depression, or headache. Most of them didn't consider the menopause a real "pause" in their lives. One woman summed it up: "I've gone through changes before, and I can weather another."

But still, a tremendous number of women, like Marianne, see the menopause as a threat. They are certainly faced with some very real physical changes. But there are also psychological changes that mount up until they create enough stress to plunge them into a life stress crisis.

The hardest part of all is that they must weather the crisis in a world that is hung up on youth. Fashions, products, life-styles, movies, television—all is slanted toward the young.

Outside the mainstream of youth, the menopausal woman sees herself threatened by her own dwindling sexual attractiveness, the loss of her children, her waning reproductive ability, poor health, and her husband's failing devotion.

Marianne, after her initial depression, coped with her crisis not by trying to hold on to her fading youth as her friend did, nor by throwing in the sponge and accepting instant old age, but by rebelling against the situation. By refusing to be placed on nature's discard heap.

She joined a consciousness-raising group of women because she felt that somewhere along the line she had missed out on life. She wanted to understand why. The group helped, not because it expanded her consciousness —it did that, too—but because it brought her into a new situation where she made new friends and was exposed to new ideas.

It also gave her the courage to try things out on her own, for instance to take vacations alone when her husband couldn't take the time to go with her. To her surprise she found that she enjoyed it. New possibilities opened up.

An important coping strategy in the menopausal years is the making of new friends, the changing of a life-style, getting involved in new activities. Some women, like Marianne, join groups that offer intriguing new approaches to life. Others, now that the nest is empty, go out into the job world.

Whatever they do, the main thing is the combination of change and activity, of getting out of the rut of a life that appears to be winding down and into something exciting, challenging, and demanding—and above all, new. Life must be starting or ongoing instead of ending.

Some women go into business. Some go back to

school. But whatever they do, not only do they cope with this crisis, but they also bring their own considerable life experience into a new area.

THE END OF PRODUCTION

For a man, the years from forty to sixty are often smooth, productive, and an emotional plateau. He has made his peace with his job and his family and these are good years. If he has divorced his wife and remarried, he may feel that this is the best time of his life. These are the years he's building a new family, a new set of relationships on the foundation of his old mistakes.

And if he has stayed in a marriage he was unhappy about, he may now accept the limitations of the marriage and work through them to a greater happiness than he thought possible.

If his marriage had been stable all along, he reaches a time, after the crisis of the forties, when he begins to understand himself, to know how far he can go and how far he can't. "I've stopped knocking my head against a wall," is the way one fifty-year-old man put it. "At least now I know what I can get out of life. Maybe it's not what I want, but it's what I have to settle for."

And then, abruptly, the long productive plateau of these two decades ends, and in his sixties a man is face-to-face with another life stress crisis, the rites of passage from work to retirement, the end of production, and the beginning of the final years.

If there is a male climacteric, as many researchers believe, it usually occurs at this time. Again the stresses mount up. There are the financial problems of retirement. Will I be able to make it? And the psychological problems. What will I do with myself now? This is a time when a man is made brutally aware that he is no longer competent in terms of the job world. He must ask himself, can I still function as a man, sexually, as a father, as a husband?

His wife, by now, has found her own independence, made her own peace with her menopausal crisis. His children are adults in every sense and no longer turning to him for help or advice. His business or job has rejected him and the world seems ready to write him off.

Studies in the *Journal of Gerontology* indicate that there are men who did very well at their jobs and got a great deal of satisfaction out of work, and still find it hard to cope with retirement, at least in the beginning. Eventually the very coping abilities that helped them handle their job so well help them to overcome this crisis and find some satisfaction in retirement. It becomes less of a period of withdrawal for them and more of a chance to do all the things they wanted to.

One of the most significant coping tools for this life stress crisis is to attempt a continuation between the years before retirement and the years after. Those people who prepare seriously for retirement beforehand are the ones with the best chance of making it unscathed. Some visit the place they plan to live in. Some develop hobbies for the years afterwards. Some begin new businesses, new lives.

John, an accountant in his early fifties, found that his job was relatively trouble free. "I'm on top of things," he told his wife. "There are no real problems on the job—or for that matter challenges. I like it, but you know, it runs so smoothly it's dull."

"Why don't you try doing something in your free time," his wife suggested. "If you had a hobby . . ."

John had always had a faint contempt for the foolish hobbies of his friends—stamp collecting, building model ships—but on his way home that evening he passed an art store and his eye was caught by a display of hard-edge paintings. They appealed to his mathematical mind, and on a sudden impulse he bought a complete set of paints.

What started as an impulse to relieve his job boredom became the main center of his life. He had a small show in his early sixties and some fair critical acclaim. When it came time for him to retire, there was no trauma or crisis. He simply shrugged off the bother of his job to devote his full time to doing what he really liked.

There was not only a sense of continuity to John's life before and after retirement, but he bypassed that deadly feeling of uselessness, the sense that life was over and from now on it was only marking time.

John's neighbor, Cameron, accomplished the same thing without a hobby. He had always been interested in community activities and after retirement he moved into community work full time. He coached a local basketball team in the evenings, did social welfare work during the day, was involved in a drug rehabilitation program on Saturdays, and in general found himself busier after retirement than before.

"I don't worry about feeling useful," he told John. "What I worry about is finding the time to relax, to go fishing, or to take in a movie."

Some men cope with retirement by continuing to work, perhaps cutting their time down to two or three days a week, but staying in the same field. They ease themselves into full retirement without ever having to make an abrupt break.

An ongoing Cornell study of occupational retirement has evaluated over two thousand men born in 1887, 1888, and 1889. A recent report of the study in *The New Frontiers of Aging* indicate that retirement may not be as hard to cope with as most people think. Many men in the United States cope with it successfully. Those in good health, well-educated, and with enough money to get by cope best!

The most important clue in predicting whether or not man can cope with retirement appears to be his own attitude before retirement. If he thinks he'll make a satisfactory adjustment—the odds are that he will do just that.

THE LATER YEARS

"September Song," from the musical *Knickerbocker Holiday* puts it very well, if sadly. "The years dwindle down to a precious few." The later years are often pathetically few in terms of a person's entire life. If we make it past seventy we count ourselves lucky. As for society—it writes us off at sixty-five.

At any age, but particularly in the years after sixty-five, some helpful insights can come from a few meaningful questions. Ask yourself:

How do I see myself physically?

How old do I feel inside?

What plans do I have for the future?

What do I want to do?

The answers to all of these will give you some basic clues about how well you can cope with the later years of life. If you are working toward something, rather than retiring from something, your adjustment will be easier. An important condition of human life is the need to go onward, to plan for the future, to become something other than what you are. If at any point in life this process stops, then coping becomes difficult, even impossible.

Dr. Herbert Klemme of the Menninger Foundation's Center for Applied Behavioral Sciences suggests that the years after sixty can be looked at as either all downhill, or the golden age of retirement. Either view is extreme, he warns, and can lead to tragedy simply because it promotes apathy, and apathy is the enemy of growth and development.

Even in these later years we must grow and develop. Life is never a simple process. We've seen that it's composed of cycliclal crises, and coping with each crisis makes us better able to cope with the next. The last, the final crisis we must cope with is the acceptance of our own death.

"How well we deal with this last great challenge," Dr. Klemme says, "depends in large measure on how well we have learned to cope with the smaller losses previously encountered."

Dr. Klemme sees coping as either a material task—how do I cope with finances, food, health care—or a psychological one—how do I end a bad marriage, find gratifying work, change my life-style. He points out that both must be managed, neither neglected.

Luke is a man who has made the mistake of neglecting both. He is what psychiatrists like to label "task oriented." He enjoys work, and given a job does it well. At sixty-five he has reached mandatory retirement age in his firm, a Midwestern printing house. Luke has always been a devoted, deeply committed worker. He sold printing to the eastern sector of the country, and there was a sincere, honest quality about him that made him very successful with the "Big City" accounts.

When he came home from the company farewell luncheon, he showed his wife a set of golf clubs, his retirement gift from the firm. "What the hell do I do with these?"

"Play golf, I suppose," his wife smiled.

"If I've played the game twice in my life I'm lucky," he said. "I'm not a golfer. You'd think they'd know!"

"Well, then, just relax. You have plenty of time to do whatever you want to now. Why don't you sit down and I'll get dinner ready."

"Why don't we go out to dinner?"

She started to protest, then looking at his tense face, she suddenly agreed. Going out to dinner was one of the few pleasures Luke had outside his job—his former job. In the weeks that followed it became obvious just how few those pleasures were. Luke was not a collector, a builder, a hobbyist of any sort. He didn't fish or hunt or enjoy any sport. Nor did he have any "inner resources." His life, quite simply, had been his job. The respect and esteem he received at the job were enormously important to him. As his wife soon realized, these things had kept him going all these years. His goals were only a more important position at work, a better salary, more responsibility.

In retirement he could find no substitutes. In one afternoon he lost all the satisfaction he had ever had in life. There was no possibility of finding another job as important at his age. There was no real joy to retirement, even though his pension and savings were enough to keep him financially comfortable.

Luke's wife had never faced quite the same problem. She had seen her children go off one by one over a period of time. She had been able to weather her menopausal crisis because it came slowly enough for her to develop other interests. She had always enjoyed sewing and needlepoint, and she began to sell her own designs to a few stores in town, not enough to make any money, but enough, as she said, to "give me a little push, the feeling that I was still useful."

When her grandchildren came she could get involved without being resented by making clothes, upholstering bassinets, embroidering, decorating—doing all the things her newly developed skills allowed, and knowing it was all useful.

Above all she found it increasingly hard to understand Luke's problems, and when he had the first of a series of depressive breakdowns, she was completely bewildered. Hadn't all the stress of his job been removed? What did he have to worry about? They were well-off financially. What more could he want?

For Luke, the real crisis of these years came at the time of retirement, and he just couldn't cope with it. For others the life stress crisis comes later, with the death of a loved one, with illness, cancer, or heart disease.

The death of a husband, wife, or close friend is often the hardest crisis of these years, and coping with it should follow certain guidelines. Mourning is an essential coping tool and is the process most people use to get over such a personal loss. The resentment, anger, guilt, and sadness associated with mourning give some release.

How well we cope with separation by death often reflects back to how well we handled our first such loss, the death of a mother or father. If we were allowed to mourn properly, to express all the feelings associated with mourning, we are usually able to cope with losses later in life.

An example of this is the classic case of the lonely old man, living by himself, who goes into a psychotic tailspin when his dog dies. But it is not the actual death of the dog that has unmanned him. It is all the other unresolved personal losses of his life that are symbolized by the dog's death. These were losses he was never able to mourn.

THE FINAL COPING PROBLEM

In the later years our entire repertoire of coping skills is demanded when we face illness, for this is a time when we realize that such illness holds our own death in the balance.

Cancer is the most dreaded disease, and the one that demands the strongest coping skills, including a type of self-deception for survival. Many people cope with cancer by refusing to admit that they have the disease. Others cope by using hope, hope of a cure, or hope that they will live a while longer.

The most successful use of hope is linked closely to

self-esteem. The more a person thinks of himself, the better his ability to hope—and the better his chance of coping with cancer.

Hope, even when it is futile, is different from denial. The person who uses denial to cope with cancer often avoids going for treatment, even when the symptoms are obvious. This is in spite of the fact that he may be aware that early treatment increases his chance of a cure.

Unfortunately, many people are convinced that coping with cancer is coping with death, and if they can deny its presence they believe they may, in some way, deny or put off death—or at least put off coping with it.

Coping with any terminal illness is simply another way of coping with your own personal extinction, a frightening problem of enormous magnitude. At first a denial of his illness gives the terminal patient a chance to marshal his unconscious, to collect some inner resources. When he must finally admit the truth, he will put up all sorts of desperate fights, hope for a miraculous cure, plea for relief of pain, or experience a sudden mystical awakening.

I had a friend who knew she was dying of terminal cancer. A few weeks before her death she experienced a "wonderful psychic experience." She told me, "I felt as if I were outside my body and I knew, in that moment, that there was a meaning to life and something afterwards."

The strength she drew from that experience gave her the strength to face the end without fear. There is another story of a terminal cancer patient in great pain who pleaded with his doctor to give him enough time to leave the hospital and attend the wedding of his son. "It will make me the happiest man in the world."

He was filled with pain-killers and attended the ceremony and celebration. Afterwards, exhausted and emotionally drained, he smiled at the doctor from his hospital bed and said, "Remember, I have one more son!"

Depression, which is often treated with drugs and mood elevators, is sometimes a way of coping with impending death. Perhaps there should be no attempt to cheer terminal patients at this point. The reality is that death is almost here. There is a dignity in depression that may be healthier than the drugged sleep of painkillers. Perhaps we were meant to meet death with such sadness.

COPING WITH A LIFE STRESS SITUATION

Can we tell just how a person will react when he is placed under unusual stress? We can never be completely sure, even when we know the person well, but to some extent we can predict how much stress the average man will take before he cracks.

Dr. Thomas H. Holmes, professor of psychiatry at the University of Washington, proposed a scale of the major life stress situations that we all experience during our lives. He assigned points to each stress, up to 100.

If you experience enough stress in one year to add up to 300, he suggests that you are close to a danger point. Among the people he studied, 80 percent who went over 300 in one year suffered serious depression, heart attacks, or other severe illnesses.

Stress Situation	*Points*
Death of husband or wife	100
Divorce	73
Separation from husband or wife	65
Jail term	63
Death of a close relative	63
Injury or illness to yourself	53
Marriage	50

Stress Situation	*Points*
Being fired from a job	47
Marital reconciliation	45
Retirement	45
Health problems of a family member	44
Pregnancy	40
Sex difficulties	39
Birth of a child	39
Change in financial status	38
Death of close friend	37
Change of job	36
Change in number of arguments with husband or wife	35
Foreclosure of mortgage or loan	30
Change in work responsibility	29
Son or daughter leaving home	29
Trouble with in-laws	29
Outstanding personal achievement	28
Wife begins or stops work	26
Beginning or ending school	26
Revision of personal habits	24
Trouble with boss	23
Change in residence	20
Change in school	20
Vacation	13
Minor violation of law	11

[CHAPTER THIRTEEN]

The Strength That Comes from the Self

THE CASE OF THE DIFFERENT TWINS

Jennie and Jimmy were fraternal twins. "They have the same coloring," their mother said fondly, "but my, they have different personalities." When asked what she meant she told the story of the mobiles.

"They're bright, glittery things and I bought them to amuse the babies, but I didn't realize they could frighten them, too. When I hung one over each crib it was funny how they reacted. Jimmy took one look and started to scream bloody murder. But Jennie, she saw it and turned away, then after a minute she peeked at it, closed her eyes, then looked again. After that it didn't seem to bother her anymore. She stared at it and stared and then began reaching out and gurgling."

Both babies coped in unique ways. Jennie let the sight of the bright mobile register, then looked away while she absorbed the image. When she was able to cope with it, she looked back without fear and eventually tried to touch it.

Jimmy couldn't handle the threat implied by the glittering toy. He coped in a time-tested way, by yelling like hell.

Both ways of coping are fine. There's nothing wrong with a baby yelling to cope with the unknown. It not only fills his lungs with oxygen, it also brings help, attention, and maybe comfort. Jennie's device was good, too. She waited out the threat to see if it was real or not. It's a case of different strokes for different folks. The twins were very different.

Consider what happens when the threat is more than visual. Let's say their diapers need changing. Jimmy yells, but it doesn't help so he tries another coping device. He stiffens his back to make the diapering difficult. Jimmy is a born resister. As a toddler he stiffens his entire body when he doesn't want his mother to put on his playsuit. He also yells.

Jennie, diapered as a baby and not liking it, took an opposite tack. She went limp as a bag of beans. "You want to diaper me? Do it. Don't expect me to cooperate." As a toddler, she still fought back with physical limpness.

Jimmy and Jennie didn't learn their different methods of coping. They were born different copers. But even so, their built-in coping patterns were strengthened and reinforced throughout their lives. When Jimmy cried, he was given a bottle, picked up, comforted. He learned that crying is a useful way of coping.

In the beginning, Jennie and Jimmy showed that they were individuals in the way they reacted to the mobiles and to diapering. By the age of two they knew what to expect when they reacted. They had a sense of the value of coping, and a sense of themselves. They were beginning to develop that great helper of coping—autonomy, i.e., self-esteem.

Their parents reacted to the twin's autonomy. They encouraged them. As the twins learned to cope they became more self-assured, more capable of further coping.

THE CHARMED CIRCLE

A group of researchers from the adult psychiatric branch of the National Institutes of Health studied the way autonomy develops through parent-child interaction and came up with a fascinating about-face of the old vicious circle concept. You could call it the charmed circle.

As a child shows his parents that he can handle responsibility, the parents develop increasing confidence in the child. The parents' confidence allows the child, in turn, to develop more autonomy, handle more responsibility. This in turn delights the parents, and on and on and on.

Another study of parents and children in a Developmental Psychology Monograph showed that the most self-reliant, self-controlled children were those whose parents were demanding, but warm and receptive.

If the parent is overprotective, the child's developing self is inhibited. If the child is shielded from life stress situations, he never learns to cope with them. If independence is encouraged by the parents, the child's coping develops more quickly.

Here are some test questions that you, as a parent, can ask yourself if you want to know just how your child's self-esteem and autonomy are developing.

1) Does your child show initiative?

2) Are you pleased and interested in the new things he learns, and do you show your pleasure?

3) Do the skills he develops—really baby skills—bore you?

4) Does your child persist in trying to be independent?

5) Do you encourage his attempts to feed himself, dress himself, clean himself?

6) Do his slow advances and messy attempts irritate you?

7) Do you encourage his curiosity and help with his investigations?

8) Do you want to change your child's will and assert your own?

Obviously there should be only three no's in your

answers if you wish your child to be strong, independent, and autonomous.

To get back to Jimmy and Jennie, the very different twins, they were born with different personalities. Does this mean they have to go through life with those same personalities, or can they change? Is there any truth to the old saw, you can't change human nature? Must we add to it, you can't change human coping?

THE LESSON FROM CHINA AND AFRICA

We know that human nature can be changed. Professor W.A.C.H. Dobson of the department of Chinese studies at the University of Toronto points to the Chinese people as an example of such a change. Comparing Chinese philosophy with Western, he says, "The Greeks were always asking why; the Chinese were always asking how. In the West we're interested in why man acts as he does. The Chinese want to know how men act as they do, and in answering that they've changed the entire direction of their society, the motivation of their people."

People who visit China today are impressed by the dedication, the devotion to their society, the selflessness and moral fiber of the Chinese. Yet forty years ago, China was a country riddled with corruption and vice. An entire nation changed its style of coping in less than four decades.

Anthropologist Colin M. Turnbull wrote about an African tribe called the Ik who were forcibly relocated from their tribal hunting grounds into a barren area by the government's creation of a National Game Reserve. Forbidden to hunt the animals that once fed them, they were forced to become farmers in a land without rain.

To cope with their new environment, they gave up compassion, love, affection, and kindness, even for their own children, and became utterly self-centered. Now the

Ik steal food from their parents and abandon the old people, the helpless infants, and the crippled with no compunction—and all of this in three generations.

How did both these monumental coping changes occur? In order to survive, the Chinese and the Ik were forced to reevaluate their own self concepts. They changed their *self*, that inner core of a human being.

This is the key to changing one's coping habits, to breaking out of whatever coping pattern we are locked into. But just what is the self?

THE LENS OF THE SELF

Most psychologists have difficulty defining self. It has been described as man's inner world, the central being of the individual. But this is a condition that can only be experienced, not defined.

When I think of self I remember a friend's daughter and her problem with it. At twenty, Katherine was slim, beautiful, and intelligent. One evening she was invited to a cocktail party in an expensive Park Avenue apartment. She went off in a flurry of excitement and returned, later that evening, in a glum mood.

"How was the party?" her father asked as she came into the room.

"The hors d'oeuvres were great, shrimp and real caviar."

"Never mind the food. What about the people?"

She shook her head. "Awful! The hostess was filthy rich—her husband was in futures or something, and there was a Hollywood producer and a writer—not just a writer, but a best-seller, and an old guy with a yacht and a jazzy blonde, a model. She was on the cover of some big magazine last month, and a hotshot lawyer who handles porno cases . . ."

"They all sound very—interesting," her mother said hesitantly.

"I guess so, but when I was introduced they all kept asking, 'What do you do?' so I told them I'm a college student, but that's not what they were after. I had to be something, or do something or have some claim to fame. Finally the hostess said, 'Well, she doesn't have to do anything, she's so pretty.' They were all relieved then; I was categorized."

Her father shook his head. "Well, tell us about the food again."

What troubled Katherine was that no one at the party wanted to accept her as a person in her own right, a young woman with no claim to fame, but who might be interesting, fun, or intellectually stimulating. This type of "self" wasn't enough. They needed the label of social status, work, achievement, or failing these, beauty.

Katherine wanted to be judged for none of these, but for herself, not her looks nor how high she had climbed the social ladder, but for her inner self, the essence of the person who was Katherine.

But perhaps it was too much to ask. We may know a person for an entire lifetime and still never penetrate to their unique, inner core. How could Katherine hope for recognition at one superficial cocktail party? How many of us have ever discovered the inner selves of our wives or husbands, children or parents?

I believe that self exists within all of us as a lens that focuses external reality upon the mirror of the soul. Depending on that lens, the reflection of the world is good or bad. Some of us see external reality, the world around us, as a hopeless and depressing condition and we find it impossible to manage.

Others see it through the lens of self as the best of all possible worlds, and they find coping a joy. Most people, however, see reality somewhere between the two extremes. Still, in every case it is the same reality. It is the lens that varies, sometimes blurring and distorting, sometimes making things crystal clear, sometimes shading everything with rose-colored tints and sometimes with a blue depression.

One psychologist speaks of the integrity of self, and sees it as the main source of strength in a person. Shakespeare wrote, "To thine own self be true . . . and you cannot then be false to any man." The late A. H. Maslow, the great humanistic psychologist, wrote that the self is strengthened by knowing and understanding it. "Your own perception of self is most important."

But how do we perceive self? How do we hear its needs? When we are tired or in pain or hungry, the self is overshadowed by the demands of our body. But when we are rested, free of pain, or full of food, then the self cries out for nourishment—and the self's nourishment is fulfillment.

THE EVIDENCE FROM THE JOURNALS

During the past fifteen years, as the concept of the self and its relationship to coping developed, there has been a tremendous amount of research aimed at discovering what the self is and what it can do. Just noting a few highlights from that research can help us understand the role of man's self.

A study in the *Journal of Personality and Social Psychology* compared people with low self-esteem to people with high self-esteem. Both were given an opportunity to cheat on a test and the results indicated that more people cheated when their self-esteem was low.

In the *Journal of Consultation and Clinical Psychology* there was a report of an attempt to discover how women felt about themselves. One of the conclusions: Women think more of themselves if other people like them. Men are less dependent on other people's estimates of their self.

Another study in the *Journal of Personality* points

out that people who don't think much of themselves are more easily manipulated.

In *Psychosomatic Medicine,* a link is found between self-esteem and illness. People with low self-esteem seem to be sick more often.

Coping, more and more obviously, appears linked to self-esteem, to how strong or weak our self is, and how highly we regard it. But how about strengthening or developing the self? Again let's look at the research.

The *Archives of General Psychiatry* published a report that young men who began to work about the age of ten acted more mature than their friends and ended up with stronger egos and "a happy sense of mastery."

Psychological Issues reports that a child develops initiative by resolving a crisis. To raise a child with a healthy personality, a parent must be "a genuine person" and the child "must not be made a victim of the parent's anxiety."

The *Journal of Social Psychology* writes up a study of Navy men. The most mature were those with the highest self-regard. The most delinquent had the lowest self-regard.

In the *Journal of Negro Education* we find evidence that when young black children are exposed to black adults who are respected members of society—attorneys, journalists, doctors, poets—the children develop intellectually and their self-esteem becomes stronger while their educational achievement rises.

And finally, *Sociometry* answers the biggest question of all as it concludes that "extreme parental indifference is more closely associated with low self-esteem than are punitive parental reactions, possibly because even punitive reactions show the child that he is important to someone."

And that, of course, is the key to the strength of the self. To be wanted. To be loved. To be cared for and appreciated all strengthen our inner self.

THE HELPING THAT HURTS

The self also grows strong through autonomy. When it's allowed to guide a person, it becomes more capable of guidance. Young children become stronger and more independent if they're allowed to work at an early age. Do too much for the growing child and you weaken the child's ability to cope. The same thing holds true when the child grows up. Do too much for an adult, and you weaken the adult's coping ability.

Raymond was married before either he or his wife had finished college. Both sets of parents got together and decided that the "kids" needed an education more than anything else in order to get a decent start in life. Neither set of parents was rich, but they managed to raise enough money to pay the couple's living expenses and tuition for the first few years.

Raymond protested, but not too strongly. "We'll get along. I have a chance at a job loading freight out at the airport."

"And pass up college?" His parents were dismayed. "Look, we love both of you and we want to make this investment in your future."

Reluctantly, the couple agreed and accepted the allowance both parents contributed, but they didn't go back to college. "What we want to do," Raymond explained, "is buy a few acres of land with the money we've saved. We want to build our own house. You said you'd send us through college. Well, we figure this is an investment for our future, too."

Uneasily the parents agreed. They kept up the allowance, and when the first baby came they helped out, too. Raymond made no attempt to find a job, but devoted himself to building the house and clearing the land.

"We suddenly realized what we were doing," Raymond's father said later. "The kids had the four of us to fall back on, and they rushed into a house and family long before they were ready for it or deserved it. We were always there for fail safe."

The four parents got together and decided to pull out and let Raymond and his wife regain their independence. "We wanted to teach them how to fend for themselves, really. But we felt awfully guilty about it."

The young couple couldn't understand their parents' desertion. "It's not fair. If we'd known you wouldn't help us we never would have gotten in this deep. What do we do now?"

Fortunately the parents stuck to their decision, and Raymond had to look for a job. They sold the land to keep going until they got on their feet again, and it wasn't easy. It took about three years before they were settled and out of debt. It also took a great deal of bitterness.

"It was the hardest decision we ever made," Raymond's father said. "But it was right, and we all stuck to it. It was the only way the kids would grow up. We made a mistake in the beginning out of love. We tried doing everything for them, and now we're paying for that mistake by being the villains. But at least now they've learned to cope with life and they're doing well."

What all the parents had overlooked when their children were first married was that real help to children comes from showing love, giving comfort, offering advice, and even making opportunities available—but never from taking over and doing things for them, never from depriving them of the right to struggle.

Without this right their inner self is crippled and their ability to cope is destroyed.

THE AUTONOMY OF SELF

Self is like body muscle. Put it in a cast or support it, keep it from working, and it atrophies. Muscle needs to work to grow strong, and so does self. It must be free to work if it is to cope—it must also be free to express its unique qualities.

But in spite of the self's uniqueness, it is driven to merge with the group. Man's original nature is to avoid isolation. The self needs to be different, but it also needs to be a part of society. We learn to cope when, like Raymond and his wife, we are given our freedom, when the dependent strings are cut—but we learn to cope within the framework of a society. In fact, we must learn to cope with that society as well as within it.

We learn self-determination even while we learn to surrender ourselves to our country, our family and friends, and eventually to our lovers. The complete autonomy of self comes when we are able to experience love, when we can merge our self with another's self. In doing this, we learn not only to love the other, but also to love our self.

Erich Fromm stressed the fact that the ability to love oneself must come before you can love another. Instead of love, you could say the same thing and substitute respect, accept, admire, have faith in—we must have the ability to do all these things to ourselves before we can do them to anyone else.

Once the self is strong enough, you can be open to experience, aware of your inner feelings, you can evaluate things and make judgments about them and you can take responsibility. With a strong self, you will be far from perfect, but you will surely be at peace with yourself. In fact you will be an autonomous man.

By definition, autonomy is the amount of self-propulsion within a person, the extent to which he takes initiative. You've heard some mothers talk about their children with depreciating pride. "He does things before he's even told," or "She goes her own way, doing just what she pleases," or "You can't push that one around. He has a strong will," or "He has a mind of his own."

We look on autonomy with pride because the autonomous man is the independent man. He is the one least likely to be taken advantage of, the one most likely to push others around, or to manipulate the world to his own advantage. The autonomous man is a "self-starter." He is self-confident and more energetic than the rest.

The autonomous child, however, is often a difficult case. We usually aren't too happy about him. Remember the different twins, Jimmy and Jennie? Jimmy was an autonomous child. When his parents wanted him to do something he wasn't happy about, he'd stiffen up and say, "You can't make me do it!"

When his grandmother heard this reaction for the first time, she shook her head. "That child is willful. Mark my word, he'll grow up spoiled unless you break his spirit."

"Mom, don't be silly," Jimmy's mother laughed. "He's perfectly right. Why should I make him do something he doesn't like, unless it's important—and this isn't."

Jimmy's father said, "The boy's tough. What's wrong with that?"

To a degree, Jimmy's parents were permissive. But they drew the line at things they thought important. As a result, Jimmy knew how far he could go, and when he said, "I don't want to do it!" far from being willful—or fresh—he was simply setting his own limits.

When Jimmy started school, he faced a completely different situation. There were very definite rules of behavior that he had to follow, not the least of which was wearing a shirt and tie to class. He had his choice of conforming or rebelling, and he chose to conform. It wasn't surprising. He had enough autonomy to know that this was a situation he couldn't beat—so he joined it. He still felt that he was his own man.

When Jimmy was in the sixth grade, he came home very excited. The school had decided that the students could vote on whether or not they must wear shirts and ties. "Oh man, what a relief it'll be to get out of this uniform!" he told his parents. He threw himself into the Free Clothes Campaign, and when it was over he was delighted that the students had won the right to wear anything they wanted to class.

The immediate result was pretty wild, but a year later his father visited the school and was startled to find almost the entire student body wearing jeans and work-shirts. "But it's just another uniform," he protested to Jimmy.

Jimmy shook his head. "You don't understand, Pop. Maybe it's a uniform, but it's *our* uniform." The important point to all the students was that this was what they wanted. They were in charge. It was their bid for autonomy.

Jimmy's twin, Jennie, hadn't been involved in the Free Clothes Campaign. She was perfectly content to follow the rules. To a degree she was autonomous, too, but not nearly as much as Jimmie even though she had had the same upbringing. In many ways Jennie was a more passive child. Even as a baby she had protested by going limp instead of stiffening up like Jimmy. But part of her coping was the ability to set her own limits. She was secure as long as she knew what she was doing. When she didn't, she never hesitated to ask for help.

SETTING LIMITS

Usually the man who refuses to accept his own limitations is insecure. He sees his limits as a potential defeat and an implied slur on his ability. Since he is insecure to begin with, he usually bites off more than he can chew.

Mr. Smith decided to build a cabin in a small vacation resort and he checked out the local builders. He found two whose price was reasonable, and presented each with plans of his house to get a time estimate. "I'd really like to have it before the summer."

Bronson told him he didn't think he could manage it in time. "There's just too much work involved, and I can't guarantee it for the summer."

Riley, the other builder, looked over the plans and nodded. "Can do."

"In time for the summer?"

"Why not?" He started off like a whirlwind, but within a month it became obvious that there was no chance of his finishing it in time.

"But you promised me," Smith protested. Riley shrugged. "It's not my fault. The weather has been bad, and you know what help is these days . . ."

Smith stewed through the summer and didn't get his house till well into the fall. He remembered Bronson's conservative approach and realized that Riley's optimism was only a reflection of his insecurity. He couldn't accept his own limits so he took on as much work as he could get.

For a man to accept his limits, he must be secure enough to say, "I can do so much and I won't agree to do more." But he must also know how much he can do. He must have a clear understanding of his ability. Riley didn't, assuming he was honest. He couldn't set limits because he didn't know how much he could do.

To look at a job and say, "I can't do that," or "I can only do half of it," or "I can do it, but not as fast as you need it," implies self-confidence and security, both basic parts of autonomy.

Riley, even though he couldn't complete the job, or botched the work in order to hurry it up, could ignore his failure and repeat the entire process with his next assignment. He copes with failure by refusing to recognize its existence. In this way he can preserve a fantasy of his own autonomy. "I'm a damned good worker because I have more work than I can handle." He also blames the weather, the material, even his assistants to explain away his own failure.

Eventually, of course, word of Riley's goofs gets out, and he loses business, but this, too, he sees as something he doesn't deserve.

As annoying as Riley's reactions may be to his clients, they serve to protect Riley's inner self. He survives by putting the blame for failure anywhere but on himself.

It would be far better, of course, if, like Bronson, the other builder, he understood his own limits from the beginning.

THE AUTONOMOUS MAN

The man who can set limits can usually manage the pressures and demands of the outside world. He's a better coper, a truly autonomous man who refuses to let any situation get the better of him, for autonomy, when all is said and done, is simply the other side of self-respect and self-esteem. The man who thinks highly of himself is the one who knows that what he does is right—and does what he knows is right. He's a self-starter, an autonomous man, He is, in the final analysis—a creative coper.

Afterword: Creative Coping

This book has presented a number of the most common devices used to cope with life, but we must remember that they are far from the only ones available. Indeed, there is as great a variety of coping strategies and styles as there are people to use them. Any problem can be solved by a dozen different approaches, and different people use different methods.

Once we develop a coping technique, we have to remember that it won't work for every situation. What worked last week with Alice may not work this week with Marie, but what we learned from coping with Alice should help us discover a way to cope with Marie.

Three men will approach one problem in three different ways. Tom sees the problem as someone else's fault. "If he did his work right, there wouldn't be a problem," or "It's not my fault that I'm having trouble."

Dick jokes about the same problem. He breaks the tension with a funny story and pretty soon the others are jollied into pitching in and helping him.

Harry brings a cool logic and reason to the problem and analyzes every angle of it, then plunges ahead to solve it.

The problem is the same one, and they all cope with it and perhaps all solve the problem according to their own needs. A fourth man might use all of the methods, plus a few more to arrive at an answer. This would be a truer picture of how all of us cope with life, if we cope competently.

In an earlier chapter we talked about aggression and how, far from being a bad coping tool, it can be an extremely useful one, and effective. The aggressive man is not necessarily a hostile or a violent man. He's a man who knows his own strength and exerts it to get what he wants. He uses his aggression in a healthy manner.

But effective as aggression is, it is far from complete unless it is blended with flexibility. In fact, of all the coping devices, flexibility is probably the most valuable. The man who approaches any problem flexibly has a very good chance of solving it.

The man who adds empathy to flexibility and aggression and stirs in a touch of reason ends up with a very tasty coping cake, and if he frosts it with fantasy it could easily make his coping wishes come true.

What we must learn is that coping is never at its best if we're content to use only one device; in fact it may not even be possible. We must select a handful of tools to match the situation. A ditchdigger who uses only a shovel won't get very far. If he adds a pickax to his repertoire, he'll dig a deeper ditch and dig it more easily.

If we wanted to set up a coping goal, it would have to manage all the stresses of life and still keep our self-esteem high while we moved forward to solve whatever problems arise. We might even set up some basic coping steps.

1) We need information. We must find out all we can about the problem to assure us that we have more than one option, more than one possible coping solution.

2) We must organize ourselves within ourselves. Grief, fear, confusion, and anger can all disturb our judgment and our coping. In other words, we have to get it all together.

3) We must be our own man, autonomous. We

must be free to act, but we must also avoid being pushed into action before we're ready.

4) We should try to anticipate our life crises so that we won't be caught with our armor down when they come.

These four steps are a start, but we must also remember that everyone uses coping tools differently. A difficult stress situation for one man is an interesting challenge to another. It's not how serious the problem is that determines our ability to cope, but the way we see the problem and the way we handle it.

References

Aronson, E., and Metee, D. R. "Dishonest Behavior as a Function of Differential Levels of Induced Self-Esteem." *Journal of Personality and Social Psychology* 9 (1968): 121–127.

Basowitz, H., et al. *Anxiety and Stress.* New York: McGraw-Hill Book Co., Inc., 1955.

Berger, C. R. "Sex Differences Relating to Self-Esteem Factor Structure." *Journal of Consulting and Clinical Psychology* 32 (1968): 442–446.

Bluhm, H. O. "How Did They Survive: Mechanics of Defense in Nazi Concentration Camps." *American Journal of Psychotherapy* 2 (1948): 3–32.

Coelho, G. V.; Hamburg, D. A.; and Adams, J. E. *Coping and Adaptation: Interdisciplinary Perspectives.* New York: Basic Books, Inc., 1975.

Engel, M. "Children Who Work." *Archives of General Psychiatry* 17 (1967).

Erikson, E. H. "Growth and Crises of the Healthy Personality." *Psychological Issues* 50–100, International Universities Press, 1959.

———. *Identity, Youth, and Crisis.* New York: W. W. Norton and Co., Inc., 1968.

Farber, B. "Elements of Competence in Interpersonal Reactions." *Sociometry* 25 (1962): 30–47.

Field, P. B., et al. "A Student TAT Measure of Competence: A Cross-Cultural Replication in Puerto Rico." *Perceptual and Motor Skills* 16 (1963): 195–198.

Gunderson, E. K. E., and Johnson, L. C. "Past Experience, Self-evaluation and Present Adjustment." *Journal of Social Psychology* 66 (1965): 311–321.

Haan, N. "The Assumptions of Coping and Defense Examined." Unpublished Paper. Department of Psychology, University of Wisconsin, 1967.

———. "Coping and Defense Mechanisms Related to Personality Inventory." *Journal of Consultive Psychology* 29 (1965): 373–378.

———. "Proposed Model of Ego Functioning: Coping and Defense Mechanisms in Relationship to IQ Change." *Psychological Monographs: General and Applied* 77 (1963): 1–23.

Hamburg, D. A., and Adams, J. F. "A Perspective on Coping Behavior." *Archives of General Psychiatry* 17 (1967): 277–284.

———, Hamburg, B.; and Degoza, S. "Adaptive Problems and Mechanisms in Severely Burned Patients." *Psychiatry* 16 (1953): 1–20.

Hinkle, L. E., and Wolf, H. G. "Ecological Investigations of the Relationship Between Illness, Life Experience and the Social Environment." *Annals of Internal Medicine* 49 (1958): 1373–1388.

———, and Wolf, H. G. "The Nature of Man's Adaptation to His Total Environment and the Relation of This to Illness." *Archives of Internal Medicine* 99 (1957): 442–460.

Holms, T. H., and Masuda, T. *Psychology Today* 5 (April, 1972): 71–106.

Janis, I. *Psychological Stress.* New York: John Wiley and Sons, Inc., 1958.

Kubler, R. E. *On Death and Dying.* New York: The Macmillan Co., 1970.

Klein, D. C., and Ross, A. "Kindergarten Entry: A Study of Role Transition." *Orthopsychiatry and the School.* New York: Family Service Association of America, 1965.

Moustakos, C. E. *The Self.* New York: Harper and Row, 1956.

Murphy, L. B. "The Problem of Defense and the Concept of Coping." in Anthony, E. J., and Kouperr, C. *The Child in His Family*. New York: John Wiley and Sons, Inc., 1970.

Murphy, L. B. *The Widening World of Childhood: Paths Towards Mastery*. New York: Basic Books, Inc., 1962.

Neugarten, B. L., and Krainer, R. J. "Menopausal Symptoms in Women of Various Ages." *Psychosomatic Medicine* 27 (1965).

———. *Middle Age and Aging*. Chicago: University of Chicago Press, 1968.

———. *Personality in Middle and Late Life*. New York: Atherton Press, 1964.

Rapaport, D.: "The Theory of Ego Autonomy: A Generalization." *Bulletin Menninger Clinic*. 22 (1958): 13–35.

Rapoport, R. "Normal Crises, Family Structure and Mental Health." *Family Process* 2 (1962): 68–80.

Raush, H. L., et al. "Adaptation to the First Years of Marriage." *Psychiatry* 26 (1963): 368–380.

Rosenberg, M. "Parental Interest and Children's Self Conceptions." *Sociometry* 26 (1963): 35–49.

———. "The Association Between Self-Esteem and Anxiety." *Journal of Psychiatry Research* 1 (1962): 135–152.

Senn, M. J. E. and Hartford, C. *The Firstborn: Experiences of Eight American Families*. Cambridge, Mass.: Harvard University Press, 1968.

Silber, E., et al. "Adaptive Behavior in Competent Adolescents." *Archives of General Psychiatry* 5 (1961): 354–365.

Smith, D. H. "A Speaker Models Project to Enhance Pupil's Self-Esteem. *Journal of Negro Education* 36 (1967): 177–180.

Stokes, R. G., and Maddox, G. L. "Some Social Factors on Retirement Adaptation." *Journal of Gerontology* 22 (1967): 329–333.

Streib, G. F. and Schneider, C. J. *Retirement in American Society: Impact and Process*. Ithaca, New York: Cornell University Press, 1971.

Tippett, J. S., and Silber, E. "Autonomy of Self Esteem: An Experimental Approach." *Archives of General Psychiatry* 14 (1966): 372–385.

Weiss, J. M. "Effects of Coping Response on Stress." *Journal of Comparative and Physiological Psychology* 65 (1968): 251–260.

White, R. W. *The Enterprise of Living: Growth and Organization in Personality*. New York: Holt, Rinehart and Winston, Inc., 1972.

———. *Lives in Progress*. New York: Holt, Rinehart and Winston, Inc., 1966.

———. *The Study of Lives*. New York: Atherton Press, 1964.

———. "Competence and the Psychosexual Stages of Development." *Nebraska Symposium on Motivation,* 1960.